What are you doing for the rest of your life?

Retirement in Ireland

By Anne Dempsey

THE RETIREMENT PLANNING COUNCIL

OF IRELAND

A Paperback Original
First published in 1986 by
The Retirement Planning Council of Ireland,
16 Harcourt Street, Dublin 2.

Reprinted 1986
Revised edition 1988

ISBN 1 85132 001 6

We wish to acknowledge the substantial funding
for the production of this book which was provided
by the Health Education Bureau.

Additional funding was provided by Irish Life
Assurance plc., New Ireland Assurance Company
plc., Pension & Investment Consultants Ltd.,
Irish Pensions Trust Ltd., Guinness + Mahon
Ltd., Shield Life Insurance Co. Ltd., Allied Irish
Banks plc., Bank of Ireland, A. Guinness Son &
Co. (Dublin) Ltd., and Prudential Life of Ireland
Ltd.

The Retirement Planning Council of Ireland
wishes to express its deep appreciation to all its
sponsors who made the production of this book
possible.

Illustrations by Stephen Hope.
Photography by the Slidefile.
Cover Design and Typesetting by
Printset & Design Limited, Dublin.
Printed in Ireland by Genprint, Dublin.

Contents

For age is opportunity no less
Than youth, though in another dress,
And as the evening twilight fades away
The sky is filled with stars, invisible
by day.

Morituri Salutamus, Longfellow

Author's Note

I have been involved with the Retirement Planning Council for a number of years as a contributor to their magazine which was then called *Look Ahead* and is now known as *Horizon*. So I was very interested when they approached me with the idea of a book to explain to people the need to prepare for retirement, and the potential for life after work.

The Council which was set up in 1976 runs retirement planning courses all over Ireland to raise awareness of the need to plan for retirement.

The book is aimed primarily at people still at work, secondly at people in retirement, and thirdly at the general public.

This new edition updates the chapter on finance, has a new look at housing provision for retired people and examines the implications of the proposed national pension plan.

Today more and more people are leaving fulltime employment before retirement age, either by taking early retirement, or more sadly due to redundancy or unemployment. We believe that the question 'what are you doing for the rest of your life?' is more relevant than ever before.

Though still in my 40s, I have a real interest in the subject, as my own husband Dave was made redundant in 1982. He now works from home, and so we have had to adjust to many of the changes facing retired couples — being together for most of the day, altered financial circumstances, new roles.

I am, however, far from expert on the ramifications of retirement and so would like to thank all the specialists I consulted who explained quite complex subjects like pensions, investment, wills, social entitlements, as well as health, diet, fitness and coping with loss.

But the most important people in the book are the retired people themselves. I met many in active retirement associations, others through friends of friends and my own journalistic contacts. Some are enjoying retirement very much, others not so well. To ensure that I covered every aspect of their lives, I devised a questionnaire which covered subjects like attitudes, money, relationships, housing and leisure. Often we strayed far from the questionnaire and I heard lots of interesting tales of life long ago. I also got a great insight into the durability of human love. I met couples in their 60s and 70s absolutely devoted to each other which is very heartening in these days. Some of the people I talked to were happy to be identified, others asked me to use a pseudonym. To them all, 'thank you'.

Anne Dempsey
April, 1988

Introduction

There is no doubt that the years when active work has ceased can be a serene, happy and fulfilling part of our lives. The Retirement Planning Council of Ireland has questioned many of the conventional assumptions relating to retirement and commissioned this book as a practical step to assist those approaching and in retirement.

The Author, Anne Dempsey, has met and interviewed a cross section of retirees and in a very readable and human way, has cast a much needed light on their actions, attitudes and concerns. She brings into focus the difficulties faced by today's retirees and each chapter suggests ways whereby the problems might be avoided in the future. It seems that those who planned for their retirement are now in a more secure and fulfilled atmosphere.

Many organisations and institutions have provided assistance and support throughout the preparation of this book. I must, however, specially refer to the financial support and encouragement provided by the Health Education Bureau particularly during the initial stages of the project. Indeed without their generous support and the financial assistance from our sponsoring organisations, the Retirement Planning Council of Ireland would not have succeeded in publishing this book.

I believe that *What are you doing for the rest of your life?* captures the atmosphere and emotions of people retiring and is an essential step in the examination of the attitudes of the Irish public and business managers about the problems, perceptions, expectations and intentions of retirement. In addition, it is a practical guide to each individual seeking to plan for a contented retirement.

Jim Kelly *Chairman*
Retirement Planning Council of Ireland
16 Harcourt Street,
Dublin 2
May 1986

1.

New Beginnings. . .

John and Mollie live less than a quarter of a mile from one another in Dun Laoire, but they've never met. He's in his early 60s, she's over 80. She's single, he's married, she's outgoing, he is reserved. But they have one big thing in common. Both are making a success of their retirement, mainly because each has made a pretty good fist of their life so far. He retired a few years ago after 45 years with the same company as a laboratory researcher. Despite her grand old age, she left paid employment only recently too, her varied working life included the catering, secretarial and retail trades.

John

John loved his job. His eyes light up as he talks about it, and he blinds me with science in a patient effort to help me understand the properties of the living organisms he worked with. But he wasn't a workaholic, and was quite happy to leave his microscope aside at weekends. John kept a bicycle at Connolly Station and cycled across to the laboratory in all weathers. In spite of his happy working life, he was looking forward to retirement. He did a pre-retirement course a few years before he left, his wife came too, and they found it very helpful: 'Most of the factual things we heard about health, finance, housing, we knew already, and a lot of it was only common sense.

'The most valuable part for us were the questions it raised about what life would be like for the two of us in retirement, how we would get on together. It was also very good to meet other couples, and there was a great feeling of cameraderie, we were all in the same boat. I notice a changed attitude these days about retirement. I remember people leaving work five to six years ago, retirement parties were sad occasions, people would be singing sad old songs and the feeling was, he is finished — done for. But these days retirement parties are a celebration, signifying the end of one thing, but the beginning of something else. I think we should come up with another name for retirement. The name implies pulling back, and it shouldn't be that'.

John is a morning person. He gets up before eight, and most days, attends mass, and takes a three mile cycle around Dalkey and Dun Laoire where he was born and reared. He gave up smoking years ago, is fit and healthy, and looks much younger than his 63 years. Almost every day from March to October he will spend some time in the garden, accompanied by his cat Henry (the path where Henry sits and stalks has 'Henry Street' engraved in the concrete). John grows flowers, shrubs and some of the more expensive vegetables like peppers, marrows, courgettes. He enjoys it a lot.

'I really can't convey to you how much pleasure I get watching insects, watching nature at work. I can just sit and look at a rose. I was a member of the Dublin Naturalists' Field Club for years, you could say I was a beetle fan from way back! You know the poem about the value of stopping and staring? Well, I'm doing a lot of that now.' One of the hobbies he always wanted to try was painting. He enrolled in a local art class, and now paints with an art group once a week. Not all his learning pursuits were successful. He took up yoga, didn't like it and dropped out. He learned wood-carving, and the house is festooned with implacable eastern faces, and graceful wooden shapes. He makes his own wines. He has converted a bedroom into a study, set up his microscope, and still works there for his own satisfaction.

It's a musical family and two of his four sons are involved in the entertainment business. John says he couldn't visualise a household without music, and he will regularly sit down with something light and classical to suit his mood. He maintains his quite personality is perfectly complemented by his warm and friendly wife. They have both separate and shared interests. Together they take off every Sunday for a drive and a picnic. Together they go to the theatre and recitals at the National Concert Hall. Together they walk from Dun Laoire to Dalkey, usually hand in hand. They don't eat out much but had an interesting gastronomic year after his retirement: 'I was on pay-related benefit for 63 weeks, and we had lunch in a different restaurant one day a week, it was great while it lasted. As a general comment, I would say we're ecstatically happy.'

When John retired he got a lump sum and a pension. He has invested the gratuity so as to achieve both regular income and capital growth. He doesn't worry about growing old, but sometimes gets depressed: 'You could call it a negative feeling. I wonder what have I done with my life, but I usually snap out of it, and realise how much I have to be thankful for'.

Mollie

Mollie Carlos's life and experiences are quite different. She grew up in Ros-common, and came to Dublin to work over 60 years ago. She has had her share of bad health, and as a single woman, a checkered career with rented accommodation in Dublin. She has moved many times; forced to leave because of rent increases, or the arbitrary sale of a house of flats. She lives now in a sheltered housing scheme, having used most of her savings to furnish the bedsitter. She gets no occupational pension, and lives on the state's old age contributory pension. She says she has never been so well off, living in low rent, comfortable and secure accommodation.

She misses work a lot. She stopped reluctantly at 75, and still misses the company of young colleagues. But she's the kind of woman who has gathered friends of all ages during her life, and she is still in constant touch with them. Mollie began gardening when she was six years old by planting a packet of marigold seeds, and watching them grow. She's had a garden wherever she's been, and one of the reservations she had coming to the sheltered scheme was how she would manage without a little plot.

She needn't have worried. In fact, her garden today probably represents her greatest achievement to date. When she came the main lawn was a mass of long grass, rubbish, brambles and weeds. Mollie asked if she could take it over, and

2

officialdom agreed with alacrity. Today the garden is a grassy sweep of lawn with all-year-round colour from spring daffodils through hydrangeas to roses. The vegetable plot has potatoes, onions, cabbages, gooseberries, chives, lettuce. She never has to buy a vegetable, and gives lots away. Mollie describes her garden as 'her hobby and her pleasure'. With a pet robin for company, she's out there stooping, digging, weeding, sowing and thinning, and the arthritis which comes on in winter is held at bay.

During the winter she knits — delicate lacy sweaters and chunky jackets. She sees her friends, keeps avidly in touch with current affairs, and has opinions on everything. Mollie is a fighter. After a heart attack, her doctor advised her to have a telephone installed in her flat. Unsuccessful in her dealings with the Department of Posts and Telegraphs (as it was then called), Mollie at 78, picketed their Dublin headquarters, and had her picture taken for a national daily paper with a placard around her neck. She had her phone within a month: 'I'll fight injustice if I have to. As far as I was concerned, the P & T had a contract with me which they weren't honouring.'

Refusing to Accept the Stereotype

Mollie doesn't worry about growing old. In her company, age is an irrelevance, and it has nothing to do with her spirit and her zest. What Mollie and John have in common is an attitude about themselves. Mollie refused to accept the stereotype that old dears of nearly 80 don't picket a government department, or buy an electric lawn mower. John has cultivated inner resources — the ability to be alone, to enjoy simple things, to stop and stare.

Every year 29,500 people reach retirement age in Ireland. Subtract from the total the 15,000 home-based women, self-employed people who work on, early retirees, and you're left with between 5,000-10,000 people who retire each year. Some do very well in retirement. A minority cannot cope at all, and death within two years of retirement is not uncommon. A large number get by. They potter about, but don't achieve anything like the potential they could from what is now becoming the last third of their lives.

Our ancestors didn't have to learn how to cope in retirement. They were dead long before it happened. In 1900, the average life expectancy for a man was 60, a woman 67. Today the average for a male is 76, for females 79. Never before in the history of man have we lived so long. Ireland has an over 65 population of 381,000 (1986 census) and growing at an estimated 10% over the next five years.

A Better Way

The implications of this huge elderly population are still not being faced in national and economic planning. We have succeeded, through medical and social advances, in adding years to the life, but not always life to the years. Issues like a national income-related pension plan, positive discrimination in favour of vulnerable elderly people, preparation for retirement, phased and flexible retirement, the housing needs of elderly people are still not being faced up to at state level.

But retirement is an individual and personal challenge too. We train for most periods of our lives, except retirement, but we will get more out of it if we plan in advance. Retirement is both a new beginning and a part of our continuing journey, as I hope in the following pages to prove.

2.

Are You Prepared?

How prepared for retirement are you? Here is a quiz adapted from the British retirement magazine *Choice* to help you find out:

1. Do you feel resentful at the prospect of retirement? Yes ☐ No ☐
2. Does the thought of no job make you fearful? Yes ☐ No ☐
3. Do you regularly take work home? Yes ☐ No ☐
4. Do you feel nobody will do the job as well as you can? Yes ☐ No ☐
5. Have you many friends outside work? Yes ☐ No ☐
6. Are you worried about how you will manage financially? Yes ☐ No ☐
7. Do you know exactly what your retirement income will be? Yes ☐ No ☐
8. Do you look forward to retirement as a time to:
   A) take it easy A ☐
   B) take up new interests B ☐
   C) a bit of both C ☐
9. How much time do you spend watching television daily?
   A) one hour A ☐
   B) three hours B ☐
   C) more C ☐
10. Do you have any hobbies that take you out of the house? Yes ☐ No ☐
11. Do you plan to expand any hobby in retirement? Yes ☐ No ☐
12. How many clubs, associations do you belong to:
    A) none A ☐
    B) one or two B ☐
    C) more C ☐
13. Are you a member of any committee? Yes ☐ No ☐
14. Have you taken up any new interests in the past five years? Yes ☐ No ☐
15. Have you attended any adult education courses within five years? Yes ☐ No ☐
16. Do you enjoy working in the garden? Yes ☐ No ☐
17. Are you reasonably fit? Yes ☐ No ☐
18. Have you deliberately done anything to improve your fitness? Yes ☐ No ☐
19. Do you do any active sports — golf, tennis, bowls, swimming, squash? Yes ☐ No ☐

5

20. Have you discussed retirement with wife/husband, family member/friend?　　Yes ☐　No ☐

21. Have you shared interests?　　Yes ☐　No ☐

22. Have you separate interests?　　Yes ☐　No ☐

23. Is housework ever shared between you?　　Yes ☐　No ☐

24. Do you plan to attend a pre-retirement course?　　Yes ☐　No ☐

25. Will you take wife/husband, son/daughter with you?　　Yes ☐　No ☐

Scoring:

1. yes 0, no 1.
2. yes 0, no 1.
3. yes 0, no 1.
4. yes 0, no 1.
5. yes 1, no 0.
6. yes 0, no 1.
7. yes 1, no 0.
8. A 0, B 1, C 2.
9. A 2, B 1, C 0.
10. yes 1, no 0.
11. yes 1, no 0.
12. A 0, B 1, C 2.

13. yes 1, no 0.
14. yes 1, no 0.
15. yes 1, no 0.
16. yes 1, no 0.
17. yes 1, no 0.
18. yes 1, no 0.
19. yes 1, no 0.
20. yes 1, no 0.
21. yes 1, no 0.
22. yes 1, no 0.
23. yes 1, no 0.
24. yes 1, no 0.
25. yes 1, no 0.

Maximum score 28 points.

28-23 points:　You are obviously on the right track for a long and happy retirement.

23-15 points:　You still have some adjustments to make in money/time or health preparation. Begin now.

under 15 points:　You have yet to face up to the fact that you're going to retire someday, maybe soon. But it's still not too late to prepare. Read on.

Looking at the questions again, you'll notice they fall into obvious categories, covering the management of money, time, attitudes, relationships and health. In preparing for retirement, there is much you can do in all these areas. Let's begin with money. When researching this book I met many people approaching retirement age who didn't know what their retirement income would be. The reasons seemed to be an unwillingness to face the prospect of retirement, a fatalistic attitude that there's nothing one can do to counteract a drop in income anyway, plus difficulty in getting information within the firm when people did delve.

Know Your Pension Rights

Every participant in one pre-retirement course I attended said their pension scheme booklet was incomprehensible. It is important to know what your occupational and/or state pension will be long before you retire. The amount you get depends on your particular occupational scheme, salary and years of service. The amount you get from the state depends on your social insurance record. Occupational pensions vary greatly from firm to firm so, find your book, dust it off and read it. If you can't understand it, bring it to your personnel department, or your union (most unions now have full-time pensions officers). The conditions for state contributory entitlement are complex, and you should not assume you will receive a state pension. Find out from your employer, or the Department of Social Welfare, but first of all, read Chapter 5 on entitlements.

One of the best reasons for knowing your pension details is that you can improve your provision while still working but not after you leave. You can top up your pension by making additional voluntary contributions (AVCs) if you have the money to spare. Always be careful, however, that you don't exceed the maximum for tax purposes. Another option while still at work, up to the day you retire, is to convert a single pension into a joint one covering dependants. Up to 15 years ago, most pensions were of the single type, and if a man died in retirement,

his pension died with him. The option for conversion was always available, but tended not to be taken up.

Joint Schemes

During the seventies, the idea of schemes with separate benefits for spouses and children came more into use. Most of the newer schemes are joint schemes. Some existing schemes give employees the choice of increasing their contribution and converting from a single to a joint scheme. If you're not in an occupational scheme at all, now is the time to approach your employer and union and discuss its introduction. If that fails, you should think about making personal financial provision for your retirement through saving and investing, taking out an insurance policy or a personal loan scheme.

This is particularly important for self-employed people, who may not qualify for a state pension, and must make their own financial provision for the future.

There are other ways of spending money now to save later. If you're staying put in the same house after retiring, you could avail now of off-peak special offers to insulate, double glaze your home and to make it more safe and burglar-proof. Eileen did this before she left work. The family home which she shares with her sister needed some major repair work so, they had it done before they retired, and now have a cosy, low-maintenance house. The cost of these jobs goes up every year, and it would be better financially to have it done now, rather than use some of your precious pension money later.

Note — keep some of the DIY jobs to help ease you into retirement.

You might be thinking of moving when you retire. You may feel the house is too big, too cold, the garden too labour intensive. Now is the time to consider options, the advantages versus the disadvantages of moving.

Why prepare at all? Basically making the best financial provision for your future will greatly determine the kind of life you have when it comes. While there are a lot of pleasures to be had for free; a walk in the park, use of the public library, a radio play — there are certain things that cost money. Putting a little variety into our days by netting a bargain at the January sales, going out to tea, or sending someone we love a present all cost money. Cash gives choice.

Adjustments

We may also have to change our attitude to retirement. Many people I met weren't prepared emotionally for retirement, and suffered hardship as a consequence. Here's how former RTE newsreader Charles Mitchel felt about his retirement: 'I felt very unhappy about it. I still had the voice and the capacity. Okay, the face gets worn out, and the hair has gone grey, but I'm just as competent, so why on earth not go on using me?' Hilary Shannon, development manager with the Retirement Planning Council of Ireland says there are three main areas of adjustment that retiring people must consider: 'The first thing you must get used to is lack of routine. When you're at work you get up at the same time, you're out all day, and you come home at approximately the same time each evening. You may have the Monday morning blues with the tail up again on Friday evening. The day, the week is shaped by work. Often we work within a structure that is rigid and

inflexible. At work everyone is answerable to someone. It's different in retirement. The body, used to waking up and jumping out at 7.30 in the morning has to adapt to a new routine. The same with the mind. Retirement brings the freedom to decide your own routine, but many people miss out on that freedom and the bonus it gives.

'Some men, for example, substitute their wife for their boss; they are like released prisoners who don't know what to do with their freedom! They want their wives to dictate their time. It would be better if that didn't happen. Retirement should mean being able to say "it's a nice day today, let's head off"; it should give the freedom to decide your own life'. He believes there should be a definite break between ending work and beginning retirement in order to stand routine on its head. A short holiday would be ideal.

The Absence of Work

The second great adjustment people have to make is the absence of work: 'Think a little about our attitude towards work. We talk about working hard, noses to the grindstone, shoulders to the wheel, a job well done. No matter how much we give out about it, we all value work. The ability to work makes us feel wanted, useful, making a contribution. Now that we're heading for retirement, we might feel we're no longer useful, no longer contributing. The reason for this is that we define ourselves by the job we do. Listen to the way we talk to one another. We don't say who we are, but what we do. People see themselves as a job, and when they no longer have that job, they can't handle the loss of identity involved. The "what" is gone, and they can't find the "who".

8

'Part of the trouble is that people may never have come to terms with "who am I?" There may be a lot of unresolved ambition inside them. We all have ideas of how far up the ladder we would like to be by a certain time. Some people retire without coming to terms with not having made it to the top. But in retirement, people can and do learn other ways of making contributions. Many have what amounts to second careers running local organisations through which they can get a lot of personal satisfaction'.

Admitting Your Age

The third adjustment people have to make is to admit their age: 'Between the ages of 50 and 70 people keep very quiet about their age,' says Hilary, 'but once they're over 70, many love to tell you — they're proud of having survived so long!' The reasons for such diffidence are, he believes, easy to understand. As a society we discriminate against older people. We see them as less capable. We say they're old and past it. It's an 'ism' called ageism, and it's quite pervasive.

'Go out and look at some of the retirement cards on sale, and you'll find them full of decrepit old men lying on hammocks. That's the public perception of retirement today', says Hilary Shannon. 'Look in your children's and grandchildren's school books and you'll see a picture of grandpa standing on a stool hammering a nail into the wall, with two people holding his legs for fear he'll fall. That's the attitude children are being taught. No wonder', he continues, 'people feel defensive about their age. The tragedy is that they accept the stereotype, take on the image, and the public perception of the retired person as old and incapable

becomes, or can become, a self-fulfilling prophecy'.

In fact, age need mean no more than a date on the calendar: 'At 65, you can still do things you did when you were 64, and you'll probably be as active and as alert when you're 70', says Hilary, 'much of it is in the mind'. Much, not all. Older people may have to accept a pair of glasses, a hearing aid. They can't run for the bus like they used (but they didn't get a free seat in the old days either). Coming to terms with age means accepting the nice things about growing old as well: 'You're your own man', says Leslie Mahon from Ballygall, Dublin, 'you can wear what you like. I call over the waiter and say "what's this stuff?" and couldn't care less.

'There is time to do what you want. As you get older, work can become a pressure. If you're a perfectionist like me, you worry. Leaving it can be a relief, I'm enjoying retirement immensely'. But retirement gives people 2,200 hours a year extra to fill, so preparation should include having some idea of how to fill it. Use the quiz as a pointer. If you have few interests outside work, now is the time to find some. There are no shortages of opportunities. The *Guide to Evening Classes* published every summer by the Wolfhound Press lists hundreds of courses beginning each autumn, most of them for interest and enjoyment.

You could learn a hobby that would be a second career in retirement. Dick Hargaden from Mount Merrion, Dublin is a pensions consultant in his 40s, and it was his day job that prompted him to take a night course: 'In my work, I've had the opportunity to observe executive stress, and to see people arriving near retirement age with no interest outside their work. I began

9

to realise the importance of a hobby, a contrast to mental activity, something I could do with my hands''. Ten years ago Dick enrolled in an upholstery class at Newpark Adult Education Centre, Blackrock, and since then he has learnt woodwork and french polishing. He now has an absorbing hobby in furniture restoration, which could become lucrative in his retirement.

Who Are Your Friends?

Surveys show that 80% of the personal contacts people have in adult life are work-related. On retirement this contact is usually broken, and loneliness and isolation can set in . This may apply particularly to the 77,000 single men and 10,000 widowers in the 45-65 age bracket, and the 60,000 single women and 53,000 widows in the same category. It's a good idea now to think of

friends in a wider way. You haven't seen old Mick or Mary in years? Look them up, they may be delighted to hear from you.

After retirement, people tend to live more in their own locality, so neighbours, family, relations, grandchildren can become important as a source of warmth and friendship. If this side of life has been neglected due to pressure of work, try and begin to establish local contacts now. Your awareness is the first step. If you have a skill you think is marketable, begin building contacts before you leave. One man I met in my travels did just that. A trainer with his firm, he offered his service on a consultancy basis before retirement, and now works for his old firm for one week every month as a self-employed person.

How Healthy Are You?

Do you drive to and from work each day, eat a stodgy lunch and slump in front of the television at night? If this has been your lifestyle for a number of years, your muscles are already under-used and losing strength, suppleness and stamina. Man is not made for a sedentary way of life and in retirement, its effects will be seen. To begin to take exercise can be difficult. Start simply. Try and park the car a little way from work, and walk a little each day. If you've time in the morning get off the train one station too soon. Go for a walk at lunchtime, or at night before bed.

Take a lighter lunch once a week, then twice a week. If you're smoking and drinking too much, have a think about it now, and try to cut down. Finally, and most important, there is the preparation for the changes you may encounter in your relationships with your nearest and dearest. Hilary Shannon says, 'For many couples,

retirement is the first time in married life since the honeymoon that they are together for so long, for such a long stretch at a time, apart from holidays. This can put a strain on a marriage. It's good to get away from each other for a while, to have separate as well as shared interests'.

Personal Relationships

We have 210,000 married couples aged 45 to 65 in this country, and 162,000 aged 65 and over. Retirement affects wife and husband, especially in Ireland. A man or woman retiring today will typically have married in their mid to late 20s, parented a larger family than the current 2.4 children, and will be active parents until their 40s or 50s. Many of the people I met retiring, still had either school-going children or sons and daughters still living at home. This long-term parental commitment affects the marriage: 'The children tend to come between you', says Bridget O'Toole, whose husband Desmond retired recently, 'you grow apart to some extent over the years, you give less time to each other, and more time to the family.' Bridget, like many women of her generation, spent 30 years at home looking after the family. She now has developed her own interests. Ten years ago, she joined the Irish Countrywomen's Association, found she was skilled in crafts and demonstration, and now has a worthwhile interest and a new line in personal development.

When Desmond retired, she felt she should be able to continue her activities, but he questioned their validity: 'He asked what the point of it all was'. Desmond didn't realise that while he got feelings of self-worth from his work, she was getting the same from her crafts. He expected her to do less

11

now that he was around, and be more available for him. She began to feel guilty about her trips into town to look at new patterns and buy wools. She began to stay in at night. Fortunately, they were able to discuss their feelings. Desmond has increased his interest in bowling, and plans to enrol in an evening course the night Bridget is out. They're still adjusting to retirement, but feel that with honesty and affection, things will work out.

Time Management

It's a problem of retirement Hilary Shannon has met repeatedly in his work: 'The delicate relationships between wife and husband demands careful adjustment in retirement. So it's important it's prepared for together. You are going to be spending more time together, so you'll learn more things about each other, some of them surprising.

'The man has to realise that while he has spent his working day away from home, his wife has filled the hours with her own occupations. She has been in control of her day. Unless role-sharing is agreed, she will still have to get on with the things that need doing in the house, and she should be free to do this in the way she has done for years. You do hear of husbands wanting to help by taking over the shopping, and re-organising the house. That's not the answer. Her friends may have popped in during the morning for coffee, and a trip to the shops is social as well as business. The man should seek his own occupations for at least part of the day.

'Each may have to adjust a little to the other, and an effort to talk and listen more will help in this. Inevitably there's a million and one jobs to be done around the place that there never seemed to be time for before, but these shouldn't be foisted on him in one go. They should be treated as they always were, except now there's more time to do them.

''You know Parkinson's Law, where work expands to fill the time available? I always think of the man who painted the fence every year. When he was working, he had the job down to two evenings a year. When he retired, it took him three weeks, because people going by could stop and say 'hullo,' he could go in for a cup of coffee, talk to a neighbour over the wall. There wasn't the same rush. And that's fine''.

Take the couple that met a different problem in time management. The husband retired at 65, but his wife had a job too, and at 61 still had a few more years to go. He didn't like being at home on his own and urged her to retire too so that they could have more time together. She didn't want to leave; she enjoyed the challenge of her secretarial job, and liked meeting friends in town. But he persuaded her, and she took early retirement. With hindsight, she bitterly regrets her move, as she is finding it difficult to settle down to the quiet home-based life her husband likes.

Retirement Preparation Courses

This situation is on the increase, as more women return to work once the family is reared. With more preparation and advice she might have stuck to her guns. Her husband could have been helped to find some activities during the day, and both their needs could have been met. The Retirement Planning Council has been running two day retirement preparation courses since 1979. The course I attended was typical. A group of women and men, all within months or a few years of retirement, some already retired, came together to learn and share attitudes.

Their common denominator was a sense of facing the unknown. They worried about pension rights, keeping busy, having enough to live on. Everyone gained something. Everyone learned of some entitlement they hadn't known about. Two of the group had had heart surgery, and the doctor's talk on health in retirement was helpful. There was a session on hobbies and part-time work, another on what to do with a lump sum.

My main criticism of the course is that it was too little too late. To hear, for instance, that pensions can be topped up with additional contributions was frustrating for people who retire in a few months. Other aspects came too late too. Much better to hear it all in your 50s when there is an opportunity to change habits and take action.

'We have an on-going problem marketing pre-retirement courses', says Hilary Shannon. 'Employers say to us "great, but how can I sell it?" In time of lay-offs and redundancies, unions are sensitive to the area of retirement, and a suggestion to do a pre-retirement course, could be misconstrued. For someone to go on a course years before his retirement, it means admitting his age, and perhaps turning off his possibilities for promotion. Then we're up against resistance from workers them-selves. They say "I don't need to plan for retirement, I've managed my life without planning so far", or they say "what's to prepare, isn't it just like your holidays?" '

It's only when people come on a course that they realise its value. The Council offers early retirement courses, and plans to introduce courses in mid-life planning. Ideally they would like to see pre-retirement courses as part of the terms of employment, with everyone attending a course ten years before they leave, with a refresher course some months before. We are a long way from that target. Less than 3% of retiring workers do a course, and there is no demand to reverse this trend.

What Can You Do?

If you want to attend a retirement course, contact your personnel department and ask them to arrange it. The Council, in addition to running their own courses, also organise in-company courses throughout Ireland where the numbers are sufficient. The cost, in each case, is borne by the company. People are encouraged to bring wife/husband/son/daughter with them — whoever is living at home and would be most affected by their retirement.

Attitudes towards retirement are no better outside work than within. The numbers taking pre-retirement evening courses offered by the VEC around the country is small.

Most people believe they don't have to plan for retirement, that it just happens. The results of such incorrect thinking are most dramatically demonstrated by the numbers of men who die a few years after they leave work: 'These men don't die from anything we can identify', says a GP 'you could say they died from boredom, or you could also say they died of a broken heart'.

USEFUL CONTACTS AND REFERENCES

The Retirement Planning Council,
16 Harcourt Street, Dublin 2.
Telephone: 01-783600

Organises in-house and public pre-retirement courses, publishes *Horizon*, a magazine for the over 50s. Individual membership £10 a year, company membership £75 to £150, depending on size.

Branches:

Waterford & South East Region:
c/o Michael Kirwan,
Adult Education Centre,
Ozanam Street,
Waterford.
Telephone: (051) 73195

Kilkenny:
c/o Pauline O'Donovan,
Smithwicks,
Irish Ale Breweries,
Kilkenny.
Telephone: (056) 21014

Limerick:
c/o Liam Leland,
31-33 Catherine Street,
Limerick.
Telephone: (061) 316655

Galway:
c/o Paddy Naughton,
94 College Road,
Galway.
Telephone: (091) 62765

Retiring a guide published by the Department of Social Welfare, Aras Mhic Diarmada, Dublin 1.
Telephone: (01) 786466.

3.

How About Finances?

Five out of ten people working today will have a pension from the firm when they retire, but only one in a hundred seem to understand its provisions. This is not too surprising. When you're young, single and the world is your oyster, negotiating a good pension scheme is way down the priority list. Ten years later — married, coping with the monthly avalanche of bills from ESB to school books, a member of the hapless PAYE section — you probably resent the deductions each month, including pension fund contributions, that reduce the amount you get into your hand.

Now with fewer family commitments, and retirement, if not around the corner, at least beyond the next crossroads, you go to examine your pension entitlements, and may be in for some unwelcome shocks. Pension schemes in general, and good schemes in particular, are relatively new. A Report prepared in 1985 by John Bristow & Terence Ryan of Trinity College estimated that 52% of employees in private industry are not covered by pension schemes. Many employees are excluded because they have yet to meet the age or service qualification of their employer's scheme so that the true figure probably exceeds 60%. The same survey reveals that approximately 40% of members were in non-contributory schemes, meaning the firm paid all the contributions, the employees none.

Pension Schemes

The firms least likely to have a scheme today include the very old and the very new. These would be small urban and rural employers — shops, garages, builders, established at a time when pensions weren't considered. These days they would include companies where employees sell on commission, and pyramid selling organisations. The firms most likely to have a scheme are those with an organisation and a structure, where unions have pressed for it, or where an employer has a caring attitude to staff.

Concerned or not, of course, a firm can only provide the scheme it can afford to service. There is no legal requirement to provide any pension at all. There is encouragement to do so, in that company pension schemes approved by the Revenue Commissioners get full tax relief on contributions to the pension fund. Many companies now have 15-20% of the payroll tied up in providing pensions. When a scheme exists, employers must pay at least one-third of the cost. Today over three-quarters of the one million PAYE workforce are in a pension scheme (April 1984 figures). Today the trend is toward contributory schemes, with employees typically paying one-third and employers two-thirds of pension contributions into the pension fund.

Many schemes negotiated today offer lump

15

sum plus pension facilities, and will have provision for employees who become disabled, and for the dependants of employees who die in service. But many workers retiring this decade are too late to benefit from these improved schemes: 'For people leaving today', says Jim Kelly, director of Pensions & Investment Consultants Limited, 'the pension can be as good as two-thirds of salary, part of which can be taken as a lump sum. Wisely invested, this will counteract the effects of inflation, and coupled with moving down to a lower tax bracket, can ensure a very comfortable retirement, and no money worries. On the other hand, a pension today can be as bad as £6 per week after 40 years of service'.

Understanding Pension Provisions

So the first thing employees planning for retirement should do is discover their pension rights. If you are in a pension scheme, contributory or not, you will have a pension scheme book. Go and find it, but be prepared not to understand it. Most people I spoke to had difficulty in translating pension provisions into concepts they could understand. Some lived in a fool's paradise for years through misinterpretation of the scheme. For instance, take the case of the recently retired sales representative, who after working for 40 years for the same firm and reading his pension book frequently, was under the impression that he would be entitled to two-thirds his salary as pension, plus the state pension on top of this.

In fact, many schemes tend to pay out up to two-thirds of salary, including state pension. Many are very taken aback when this is explained to them a few months before retiring. They are more upset when

they go to collect their state pension and learn they don't qualify. So the action to take is to sit down with someone who understands and work out what your pension will be. Your adviser could be from the personnel department, the company secretary or investment manager. Many of the unions now have full-time staff, expert in pension provisions, who could explain.

Alternatively, workers could approach management and ask them to send a representative from the pension consultant firm to explain their provisions to them. Where pensions are concerned, ignorance is folly, and it's better, if not blissful, to be wise.

How Are Pension Schemes Calculated?

Most give a proportion of final salary for each year of service up to a maximum of 40 years. The proportion is typically one-sixtieth, so a man who works in the same firm for 40 years, gets forty-sixtieths, that's two-thirds of final salary. How does this work in practice? Take the man that worked for the same wine firm all his life, and was earning £15,000 at retirement. Calculating his pension as forty-sixtieths or two-thirds of this, he gets a pension of £10,000. But as explained before, this £10,000 is made up of part occupational pension, and part state pension making a total of £10,000 between the two.

Most schemes allow employees to take part of the pension as a lump sum — up to a maximum of one-and-a-half times one year's salary. When this is availed of, the annual pension is reduced accordingly. For instance, if our wine employee decides to take a lump sum plus pension, the sum is £22,500 (one-and-a-half times salary), the pension will then work out at £7,500 a year. Many people opt for this cash and pension combination. The lump sum is tax free (while pensions are taxed), and it can be invested to give income and/or capital growth.

If a woman starts working later on in life, say at 45 and retires at 65 on a salary of £12,000, her pension will be calculated in the same way that's, one-sixtieth for each year of service, in this case, 20 years. So she gets twenty-sixtieths, or one third, that is £4,000 annual pension. In this case her company will only offset twenty-fortieths (i.e. one-half) of the basic state pension. After 20 years service, she still qualifies for a full lump sum (below that time the sum is reduced). Here it would be £18,000, one-and-a-half times her salary, the annual pension reducing accordingly to £2,000.

Other Standard Provisions

Most pension schemes today have other standard provisions, such as paying a sum to the family of an employee who dies in service. Terms vary; the payment could be a lump sum equivalent to four times salary, plus a pension of 50% of salary to the dependants. It could be as low as a once-off payment of one year's salary, with no continuing pension at all. But most pensions are guaranteed for five years, so that if someone dies within five years of leaving work, it continues to be paid to the family for the balance of this period.

The majority of schemes negotiated today are joint schemes, providing for a man's family as well as himself. If a man dies in retirement, his widow will receive half his pension until her death. This joint type became common only during the 1970s. Prior to that, when a man died, his pension

died with him. When new joint schemes became established, employees were given the option of converting from single to joint: 'It was a very difficult decision to make', says Jim Kelly, 'converting to a joint pension means a man takes a 15% reduction on his pension in his lifetime, knowing that half the pension will go to her on his death. Many workers didn't know what to do for the best.

'For example, take a man who could expect a single pension of say, £4,000 a year. To convert that to joint would mean he would only get £3,400 a year in his lifetime, and she would get £1,700 a year should he die before her.' Jim Kelly maintains that the facility to convert to joint scheme is now well known. Employees are doing it, though still in small numbers: 'Many men are leaving things as they are and not converting because social welfare benefits have dramatically increased in the last ten years, and the state contribution is now becoming a sizeable proportion of many pensions.

'Secondly, people are reluctant to accept a lower pension when they can't foresee the future and thirdly, many men now feel that the lump sum wisely invested, coupled with a state widows' pension will give their wives a satisfactory income should they go'. Each employee has to make up his own mind whether it would be desirable to convert from a single to a joint pension. Knowing the facility exists is the first step.

Improving Your Pension Scheme

What else can you do while still at work to improve a poor pension scheme? An option already referred to in the last chapter is the facility to make additional voluntary contributions (AVCs). Many schemes have the facility to increase the rate at which you contribute, so that benefits can be improved. Some non-contributory schemes give the option of making voluntary contributions also, and because full tax relief is allowed on pension contributions (up to 15% of earnings), these can be very attractive from a tax point of view.

Amounts secured as AVCs are treated in the same way as main scheme benefits — they are locked in and may not be used except on death, retirement or withdrawal from work. They can be used to improve one's financial position in the following ways: to improve the basic pension, to improve the tax-free lump sum, to provide or improve a dependant's pension. Obviously the earlier these extra payments begin, the more they will buy. But, because of the tax concessions, it can be beneficial to make AVCs even for a single year. It is well worth investigating whether or not this facility exists as an option in your scheme.

Index Linking

The majority of pension schemes in the private sector are not index-linked, which means they do not keep pace with inflation. For instance, Neville retired in the early sixties from a confectionery firm with a pension of £30 per week: 'not bad at all then', he says. Today, his £30 is worth about £3 in real buying power. Some people become increasingly dependent on their contributory old age pension, with the firm's portion dwindling to provide a few small extras per week.

It has been a major criticism of private sector schemes that they are not index-linked, but this situation is changing. An Irish Association of Pension Funds survey in 1981 showed that 72% of members were in schemes which provided for some adjustment to pensions after retirement. There is no legal requirement, however, to keep abreast and where employers do make ex-gratia payments to retired workers, it is an informal arrangement which could stop at any time. At present, there is no standard system of review for private sector pensions.

Employees in private schemes face another hazard. The collapse of some companies in recent years showed that management hadn't been paying its share into the pension fund. As well as losing their jobs, many employees lost out on pension rights. How can you be sure your employer is keeping his end of the pension deal? Some firms give workers a yearly statement from the trustee manager, (the representative from the pension fund managers) setting out the value of the investments in the fund and including extracts from the audited accounts of the fund. These are the kind of safeguards employees should look out for.

Public Service Pensions

Public service pensions are expressed differently from private schemes, and there is a standard arrangement throughout. Typically, a civil servant gets a lump sum of up to one-and-a-half times final salary, based on years of service, plus an annual pension of half annual salary, again dependent on length of service.

Joe retired from the prison service last year. He was earning £18,000. He got a lump sum of £24,000, and receives an annual pension of £9,000 during his lifetime. He contributed to a widows' and orphans' attachment fund and should he die before his wife, she will get £4,500 a year during her lifetime. Civil Service salaries are index-linked, so that when prison officers get a salary increase, Joe's pension will go up in proportion. This gives him some inflation proofing.

That's the good news. The bad news is that public servants do not qualify for a state pension, and those who retire on low pay, may have to manage on quite small sums,

19

without a state slot to supplement their weekly income. Take one civil servant who retired on a low pay. His salary was £7,000. He got a lump sum of £10,500, and a pension of £3,500 a year. Unable to qualify for a state pension, he has to invest his lump sum carefully so as to provide regular cash to top up his income. Even so, he is losing on capital growth and doesn't consider himself well off after a lifetime of service.

Income in Retirement

But many people overestimate the amount of money they will need in retirement, and often worry unduly about the future. 'This', says Hilary Shannon, 'is because when calculating what their retirement income will be, they compare it with gross rather than net salary'. He suggests that everyone approaching retirement should take a sheet of paper and divide it in half. On one side, write down current gross salary. From it deduct tax, PRSI, pension fund contributions, union dues and the cost of going to work in transport (running costs and depreciation), lunch, clothes, and any personal extras. The difference between the two gives disposable income, as distinct from gross salary. Then do the same on the retirement side of the page.

Write down occupational and state pension, make the necessary tax deduction if moving down to a lower tax band on retirement to arrive at a real disposable income in retirement. The difference, he suggests, may not be very great: 'People never know how they stand financially unless they sit down and do this kind of sum'. It is the kind of information workers need in order to help them decide what amount of pension to take as a tax free lump sum, and how to invest.

Lump Sum

When Declan Sheehan got his lump sum of £20,000 he didn't know what to do with it so he took it straight away to his bank manager and asked for advice. He was sent to the bank's investment department, and within a quarter of an hour, his affairs were settled. Acting on the advice given, he invested £10,000 in an income bond which then paid 10% tax free, giving him an income of £83 per month. The remaining £10,000 went into post office saving certificates which will become £16,100 after five years. Declan is delighted. 'I tell everyone to go to their bank manager. I was worried about how to invest my gratuity wisely. I had never so much money in my possession before, and didn't know what to do with it. I felt a great weight off my mind to get it all fixed up so easily, and I think I have invested wisely, as I'm getting both an income and capital growth.'

One man's bank manager wasn't at all forthcoming with advice on different options so, he finally went to a pension broker who sat down and drew up a list of choices, with examples, to help him decide. And worse still some people put their retirement cheque into a drawer at home for six months because they don't want to rush into a hasty decision. This action loses them hundreds of pounds in bank interest which they can never recover.

What To Do With It

So what do people do with their lump sums? 'A frightening number just stick it into a building society or a bank deposit account and leave it there', says John Aldridge, insurance and investment pension consultant. 'There are unbelievable differences in the amounts that money can earn, depending on how it's invested. Many people aren't getting the full value from their money because it's not invested in a tax-efficient way'. He is all in favour of people taking their time in deciding how they should proceed: 'Don't commit yourself too soon. When you retire, you should give yourself time to adjust to a new lifestyle and a change in income. You need to see how you're managing so, you invest in a way best suited to your needs. Dick Cuddihy of Pensions & Investment Consultants Limited says, 'people investing at retirement age need absolute security, a degree of flexibility, and probably periodic injections of further income to combat the effects of inflation on a fixed pension.'

John Aldridge agrees, but says investors tend to over-emphasise the importance of having access to their money, and can sacrifice financial return to this accessibility: 'People want to be able to get at their money especially in the case of emergencies, so, they put it all into a bank or a building society, which pays a lower rate of interest than some of the other institutions, whereas they could spread it around leaving some ear-marked for emergency and accessibility. For example, £5,000 out of £20,000 buys an awful lot of emergency'.

How to Invest the Lump Sum

Each retired individual or couple will have their own needs. With a good pension, people often decide initially to go for capital growth. This can change later to an arrangement which gives a monthly or half-yearly income if more regular extra income is needed. If the pension is low, the lump sum may be needed to provide income right away.

There are a variety of institutions out there all waiting for your money, all wanting to convince you that they offer the best return. In order to assess claims and counter-claims, people must do their own homework, and decide what's best for them. At first glance, the investment jungle seems daunting, but with a little study, charting a way through it is not too difficult. There are four main options — to invest money in one of the An Post saving schemes, in the Bank, in a Building Society or with an Insurance Company.

Which will be best for you?

One way of finding out is to take a theoretical lump sum of say £10,000 to be invested for five years, paying tax at the standard rate of 35p in the pound, and examine how it would grow in the various schemes. Capital growth will vary between the four, depending on the differing interest rates offered by each institution at the time of your enquiry. But for many people, capital growth isn't the only consideration, and these are some of the other points to consider when choosing a scheme.

When you look at the results of your exercise, you can easily spot those institutions giving the best financial return. But, as mentioned, many people have other considerations: availablity, convenience, familiarity, security. The best answer may not be to put all your financial eggs in one basket, but to spread them around.

Guaranteed Income/Growth Bonds — These are insurance related products whereby funds are invested for a fixed period, e.g. three or five years, with a guaranteed rate of return. Return of the capital is also guaranteed at the end of the term. There

AN POST:

Saving Certificates

Advantages: The post office is local, near, familiar. Saving units in whole or in part may be taken out at any time with accrued interest added on.

Disadvantages: To get the full benefit, the sum must be left in for five years. If taken out before that, there are penalties.

Index-Linked Saving Scheme

Advantages: The amount can be withdrawn within seven days notice. There is no penalty, provided the sum has been left in for a minimum of one year.

Disadvantages: You may not get as much for your money as you could elsewhere.

Index-Linked National Instalment Saving

Advantages: There is ease of withdrawal with seven days notice needed.

Disadvantages: There are penalties for early withdrawal, however, with interest declining if sum is withdrawn within five years.

Index-Linked Savings Bonds

Advantages: These last for a three year term providing a tax-free growth.

Disadvantages: Penalties are suffered on early withdrawal and the maximum holding is £25,000 per individual.

COMMERCIAL BANKS AND TRUSTEE BANKS:

Deposit Accounts

Advantages: You can withdraw money at any time without penalty. It is secure, convenient, you may hold a number of accounts, and can transfer as you wish from deposit to current, plus using it to avail of other bank services such as, paying bills by direct debit, and having 24 hour access to cash.

Disadvantages: You may not get as much for your money as you could elsewhere.

BUILDING SOCIETY:

Deposit Account

Advantages: The money is accessible and secure.

Disadvantages: You may not get as much as you could elsewhere in an equally secure medium.

Monthly Income Share Account

Advantages: Regular income if needed, and the ability to withdraw without penalty at any time.

Disadvantages: You may not get as much as you could elsewhere.

is no tax liablity to the investor on these bonds. Some companies issue tax relief certificates and tax relief may be claimed in the first year of the bond on part of the premium.

Investment Bonds (Unit-linked bonds) — These are insurance linked investments with no guarantees relating to capital, income or growth. Funds are invested in stocks and shares, property, gilt edge securities and cash. Managed Bonds offer the investor the opportunity to spread his funds over a diverse pool of Irish and overseas investments and to avail of professional fund management. Returns on these funds are free of tax to the investor. Rates of return can vary up and down. For best returns, funds should be invested for at least three years. A regular tax-paid income may be taken from these bonds. As most life insurance companies issue these bonds as life assurance policies, tax relief may be claimed in the first year of the bond in accordance with the usual limits.

Finally, you also have direct investment in the stock market, investment in unit trusts or direct property investments. The personal investment market can be a bewildering morass to the uninitiated and it is strongly recommended that you use the services of an independent professional intermediary to guide and help you.

In the past some less than honest brokers lost people's life savings by not investing the principle, and thereby giving bonds a bad name: 'If you're dealing with a broker, no matter how reputable', says John Aldridge, insurance and investment pension consultant, 'always make your cheque out to the financial institution, and not to the broker. Within weeks you should receive papers and receipts of your transactions from the insurance company'.

Get Advice

Your employer may be helpful or he may refer you to his advisers e.g. pension consultants or accountants. The bank manager may be in a position to give you details of some of the investment opportunities. Insurance Brokers who are members of the C.I.B.I. or N.I.B.A. may specialise in investment advice. Safeguard your nest egg by dealing only with someone who has been personally recommended to you and who has considerable experience in dealing in this field. Finally, remember that your adviser gets commission from the institution with whom you invest.

Employees without Pension Schemes

How can those outside the occupational pension structure plan for their retirement? We have 240,000 self-employed people in the country. We have 120,000 full-time farmers, and an estimated 60,000 part-time farmers, for whom retirement poses particular problems. In the 1988 Budget proposals, these people may now receive a retirement pension. There are thousands employed in firms with no pension scheme.

How do you improve your position if your benefits are either low or non-existent? Well, if a firm doesn't have a scheme, you should press for one. Your union, if you're in one, should be on your side, though unions have been short-sighted in pressing for pension reform. Jim Kelly says, 'employers do respond to requests from employees to start a pension scheme.' One of the reasons why progress has been slow is that employees haven't pressed for a pension, many concentrating on short-term interest: 'There have been cases of employers trying to organise something', says Jim Kelly, 'they set up a contributory pension scheme with employees paying a few pounds a week (less when tax relief is granted) only to find many employees not taking up the valuable benefit of membership as it means a small drop in take-home pay.'

People with no pension scheme and no likelihood of obtaining one through the firm must try and make their own financial provision. This would include personal saving and investing, taking out an endowment insurance policy, or organising a personal pension scheme.

The Self-Employed

We have already considered investing the lump sum. Now we look at life for the self-employed person, and consider the investment of smaller annual sums.

The 240,000 self-employed people in the country include family businesses, farmers, garage owners, doctors, shopkeepers, accountants and more. The business can be as big as a factory giving good local employment, or as small as a one-person band working from home. What the group is likely to have in common is no proper financial provision for retirement. Many are workaholics and plan to go on until they drop.

'80-90% of self-employed people have made no pension provision for themselves', says Myles Tierney of the Irish Federation of Self-Employed. 'They have a mental block about it; when they're building up the firm, they say they can't afford to invest money in a pension fund. The most common remark is "sure if anything happens to me, she'll have the house and the business". What they don't realise is that if anything did happen and she had to sell out, the value of the business, the stock, the house, the car would bring her into the capital gains tax area where she may have the taxman on her head, and could fare badly.

Difficulties of Planning

The self-employed person has other difficulties as he grows older. He may indeed wish to step sideways, to wind down, to transfer the business within the family. But if he transfers, he may be liable for capital acquisitions tax. Myles Tierney believes that this tax is bad for the country because it keeps too-old hands at the rein, and can stultify fresh new ideas wanting to percolate upward. Bad for individuals too, it freezes action — 'who is going to transfer if it means handing over thousands of pounds to the government just to do so?' he asks.

The irony is that good planning for the self-employed makes great financial sense, both today and tomorrow. All payments towards a personal pension scheme up to certain limits are allowable in full against a person's top rate of tax. Tax relief, in practice, amounts to a state subsidy on contributions, and personal savings from after-tax income don't give as good a return as pension fund investments.

The Federation of Self-Employed

The Federation of Self-Employed offers a package of financial advice and help to members, including a pension scheme operating through a firm of pension consultants. The particular plan offers a choice of investments. Contributions are invested in funds which are free from income and capital gains taxes, and can be invested in either a managed fund or a cash deposit fund.

A managed fund consists of holdings in property equities, gilts and cash. Unit prices and the value of the pension investment depend on the value of these underlying assets, but the broad spread of investment in the funds tends to keep the risks to an acceptable level, while good management aims to promote the best return. A deposit fund consists of cash deposit and short-term government securities. This fund gives stability and steady growth. Often an investor will cash in managed fund holdings a few years before retiring, and invest the proceeds in the more secure deposit account.

For self-employed people, or partners in a firm, the limit for tax relief is 15% of annual earnings, less allowable expenses. For company directors, there is no contribution maximum, except that the final retirement pension must not be more than two-thirds of annual salary. The tax free status of a personal pension fund allows monies to build up rapidly, which maximises the returns at retirement.

Table 1: The following is an example showing the accumulation of an annual contribution of £1,000 to the age of 65. It assumes a steady growth rate of 10%, and

annuity of 14% which may well be bettered at time of individual arrangements:

Age At Next Birthday	Contributions	Estimated Pension Per Year At 65
30	£1,000 p.a.	£41,675
40	£1,000 p.a.	£15,143
50	£1,000 p.a.	£ 4,974
60	£1,000 p.a.	£ 1,060

These figures illustrate dramatically the value of planning early for retirement — the benefits dwindle steeply as each decade goes by.

Policy holders may retire at any time between 60 and 70. For the self-employed person or partner, up to a quarter of the accumulated funds can be taken as tax free cash. In the case of a director, who is strictly speaking an employee, the maximum tax free cash allowed is calculated as one-and-a-half times final salary, and on a sliding scale if service is less than 20 years.

The balance of the fund is used to provide a pension which is taxed as earned income. But there are flexible provisions here too. People may decide to maximise income in the early years by choosing a basic non-escalating pension for one's own life only, and it can be arranged to provide for increases in the cost of living. Or a pension can be arranged to be paid to the insurer's family in the case of her/his death. Another option for people having to provide for their own future is to take out an insurance policy that matures on retirement.

Table 2: This is how our same £1,000 paid as a yearly premium would perform, based again on a growth rate of 10% and an annuity rate of 14%.

Age Next Birthday	Estimated Pension Per Year to 65
30	£38,000
40	£14,000
50	£ 4,710

Table 3: This is how the small investor paying an insurance premium of £100 per year would fare:

Age At Next Birthday	At 65
30	£3,870
40	£1,402
50	£ 471

Insurance companies say there is little point in taking out an insurance policy at 60, when other forms of savings will give a much better return for one's money.

In thinking about retirement provision, these are the questions self-employed people should ask themselves:

How are you going to live when you retire?

How would your family manage if you died tomorrow?

Could you survive financially if you became ill?

Are you paying too much tax?

Are you sure that your savings, if any, are working to their best effect?

What should you do? Contact an insurance broker or a pension consultant who comes recommended and begin to make provision for your future.

USEFUL CONTACTS AND REFERENCES

Your Guide to Pensions by Colm Rapple, Squirrel Press, £1.95

The Irish Federation of Self-Employed,
21 Mespil Road,
Dublin 4.
Telephone: (01) 602644

FISC (Financial Information Service Centre)
87-89 Pembroke Road,
Dublin 4.
Telephone: (01) 680400

A voluntary organisation which provides confidential financial advice including tax advice, free of charge to people who can't afford their own accountant. Ask at the library for address of local centre.

4.

Can Farmers Afford to Retire?

Six years ago at the age of 65, William Patterson sold the family farm that his own father had bought in 1908, and with the proceeds bought a 200 acre farm for his son and growing family, and a bungalow for himself amid the rolling hills of County Kildare.

He has handed over the reins, but he hasn't retired. A widower, he looks after himself capably; vacuums, sews, irons and cooks. He has a well-stocked vegetable garden, and supplies himself and his married daughter who lives nearby. 'I haven't enough time in the day to do all I want', he says. 'I've had no adjustment to make because I'm still involved in my son's farm. In the busy seasons, spring and autumn, I'm there every day from early morning to late at night. I do all the combining, the ploughing, although since I put out some discs in my back I'm not able to throw around the sacks of artificial as well as I used. My son and I work together very well. We tend to agree on what should be done and how to do it. I'm at his beck and call, and I'm the first one he contacts if he has a problem'.

Handing Over

William says that at the time he was 'unusual' in getting out and handing over so early. 'When you hand over at the right time, you're still able to keep a watching brief, and you can retain a sense of continuity. Very many farmers still fail to hand over and it creates many problems. When a son reaches 30, he doesn't want to be the boy around the place any more. He has ideas — he wants to begin doing some of the things his way. There is a moment when he is ready, and if you let the moment go by, it can do damage.

'Relationships can get very sour. Many young men have been driven off the land, or they stay and become indifferent and neglectful. I've seen places which have been let go, and it's a terrible shame to see thousands of pounds worth of machinery rusting out in all weathers with the hedges uncut. The reason sometimes is because the old man is holding on too long and won't hand over ownership or decision-making. It's a terrible waste'.

There are good reasons, according to William why a man approaching retirement age finds it difficult to do so. If relationships are bad, the father could worry how he would fare as his son's pensioner, there is the question of where he would live, and above all, what he would do. 'Many farmers of my age have no interests whatever outside the farm', said William, 'they would be lost without the work, the contacts, the interests,' He had been a keen sportsman all his life, and a great committee man and feels that this long interest and participation in sport has kept him fit and involved. He loves books, particularly old books, and

27

showed me some of the volumes which have been passed down within his family for generations.

Financially William makes out. Six years before he retired he began contributing to a personal pension plan, and now has a small pension which meets his needs. 'I'm very thrifty, always have been and never waste a thing. It would have been better if I had organised a pension years ago, but there is so little return from farming, that most people aren't in a position to do it when they should.'

Inheritance Survey

As a farmer, William is still fairly unusual

28

in being willing to hand over the reins earlier rather than later. An inheritance survey of 1972 found that only 35% of farmers acquired ownership before the age of 30, and 42% were over 35 at the time of succession. It has also been shown that 25% of farmers are aged 65 or over, confirming the late age of transfer and succession. A similar survey today would give a more mobile picture. There are 120,000 full-time farmers in the country, and up to 60,000 part-timers. These days, a sizeable minority do retire, though there are regional disparities.

Retirement moves are greatest in the east and south of the country, least in the west and north west, where there would be many bachelor farmers with no heirs hence, no incentive to move on.

Farm size also plays a part. 60% of Irish farms are less than 50 acres, well below the level deemed by the Agricultural Institute as being economically viable. When farmers do retire, the arrangement works best when succession procedures are drawn up legally by a solicitor, and this is now happening to an increasing degree. Sometimes the son will build a home for his parents, (and there may be grants or loans available for this) sometimes the son and family build a house for themselves with parents staying on in the family home. Sometimes son and family rent nearby.

The FBD Scheme

Handing over the farm helps the parents' entitlement to the non-contributory old age pension, which is means-tested. Since 1988 farmers may qualify for the contributory old age pension. Very few farmers had any personal pension provision, but this is now improving. Ten years ago FBD Life and Pensions Co-Operative Ltd introduced a pension scheme specially geared to the needs of farmers. This scheme was tailored to the erratic earning pattern of farmers, allowing variable premiums to be paid, depending on good and lean times. Other pension consultants have subsequently chased the farming sector, and these days a growing number of farmers, particularly younger men, are making personal pension provision.

The FBD scheme allows the farmer to invest up to 15% of gross taxable income, and the amount invested each year may vary according to personal circumstances. The investments are used to build a fund to provide farmer and dependants with a pension from the date of retirement, which may be anytime from 60 to 70. In this context, retirement doesn't mean stopping working, but a time to start drawing from the pension. There is also the option of taking up to one quarter of the total in a tax-free lump sum.

Table 1: The following example is based on level contributions of £1,000 per annum but as has been said, these may vary from year to year.

Age Next Birthday	Contribution	Pension At 65
35	£1,000 p.a.	£24,824
45	£1,000 p.a.	£ 8,627
55	£1,000 p.a.	£ 3,383

The annual pension with tax relief of 35p in the pound involves a real outlay of £650. The growth on rate is 10%, the annuity rate 14% on retirement, and actual returns which individuals may expect when taking out their own pension plan may be much better.

29

Resistance to Retirement

But despite the changing attitude on the part of many farmers, there are many more who are still resistant to the idea of retirement and transfer. Today, less than 10% of farmers are under 35, one half of all farmers are aged 55 and over and a quarter of all farmers are 65 or over, accounting for about five million acres of land. Why do so many farmers find it difficult to relinquish the reins? 'There is an historical connection where land is very important to the Irish man because of our dispossessed background,' explains Gerry Gunning, from the rural development department, of the Irish Farmer's Association, 'Ireland has the highest rate of owner-occupier land in Europe. In Ireland 3% only of the total land area changes hands every year, and 80% of this is in inter-family transfers. Very little land comes on the market, proving the idea that holding on to the land is sacrosanct.

''Because many farmers get land at a late stage themselves, in their 40s, they say 'I'm going to hold on for as long as I can'. Farming is a seven day a week job. Many farmers, particularly the older men, never take holidays, they're not geared to leisure, they haven't been able to afford holidays, and farming is the only life they know. When a farmer retires, he loses his social outlets; the visit to the mart and creamery, which is part and parcel of his life, when he retires, he's out of all that. Then, some farmers feel if they hand over, their son won't look after them properly, and they don't want to be their sons' pensioners.

Consequences

'The effect of this', he says, 'is that younger men can't make plans for the future, marriage plans may be impeded. A young wife may be reluctant to come into a farm where the future is not secure. There may be a loose wages arrangement — £30 to £40 for the son, not enough to live on. In these cases, the young man's interest in the farm may diminish, he may get a part-time job.' All this can create great bitterness and bad family feeling, augmented when the father attempts a very late transfer, or worse, dies before any legal transfer is made. When a man dies without a will — if the farm is divided among his children — it can become a parcel of non-viable holdings, in effect, no farm.

'Even when a father does hand over, daughters and sons already left home, may have to get a financial share from the inheriting son, who may have to borrow to pay them, and begin his ownership in debt'. The national effect of poor succession policies has contributed to farm under-utilisation, neglect, and the waste of one of our great natural resources — our land. Over the years the government has attempted many national schemes to encourage or coerce farmers to hand over and retire. Generally these have been unsuccessful.

Government Schemes

A national pension scheme introduced under the 1965 Land Act aimed at inducing elderly and incapaciated farmers to retire and offer their lands to the Land Commission for structural reform. The scheme was a failure, and encouraged only 39 farmers to retire out of 400 applications. Farming journalist Des Maguire, author of *The Land Problem* believes the scope of the plan was too restrictive and level of benefits too limited. The pensions offered were based on the actuarial equivalent of the

30

purchase price, which took no account of the value of the natural asset being surrendered for restructuring purposes.

In 1974, this national scheme was replaced by an EEC plan. Known as the New Voluntary Retirement Pension scheme for farmers, it was introduced by the government to comply with EEC Directive 160, which obliges all EEC members to provide a retirement scheme for farmers. Under this scheme, farmers could dispose of their property in three ways: through sale to development farmers, through long-term lease to a development farmer, or by selling directly to the Land Commission. This scheme again attracted only a few hundred participants. It had the effect of penalising many farmers for retiring. Its benefits failed to keep pace with the non-contributory old age pension, and retired farmers were not eligible for most of the fringe benefits available to many pensioners — free travel, medical card, electricity allowance and so on.

According to the Irish Farmers' Association, the scheme would have been more attractive if the incentives had been updated to keep pace with inflation. Des Maguire believes a successful farm retirement scheme should be based on the following principles:

The annuities should continuously outstrip social welfare payments, with some fringe benefits attaching.

Where two single people e.g. brother and sister live on the same farm, their pensions should be equated with that for a married couple.

Part of the income arising from sale or lease of farm by a retiring farmer, should be free of tax: 'The state requires the land to get more production from it', he says,

'and like any other natural assets taken over there must be a price for this'.

In the less favoured areas, farmers aged 55-65 transferring to a suitably qualified heir should be allowed into the scheme.

Similarly, the upper limit of 45 adjusted acres which applies to farms eligible for participation should be abolished to allow more land to be released for restructuring.

He believes we need a much broader scheme if any of the five million acres owned by farmers aged 55 and over, are to be mobilised for restructuring.

New Trends

There are, however, some healthy new trends. The IFA had long been campaigning for long-term leasing of land. In the past, based on Land Acts of the last century, farmers could lease land only for eleven months of the year, otherwise the leasees could claim squatter's rights. This was very unsatisfactory, and limited the amount of land coming on the market for farm leasing. But since the 1984 Land Bill, long-term land leasing is now allowed. It is having the effect of ensuring guaranteed income and ownership protection for the leaser. A large amount of land has been made available for leasing since the Act was passed, and this is allowing young farmers who can't afford to buy, to lease land, hence bringing younger generations into farming.

There have been other moves. It had long been recognised that a phased type of farm inheritance — where the management and ownership would be gradually transferred from parent to heir over a period of years — might work better than the present system, where ownership of the entire farm is transferred in a day, and often on the parent's death to a nearly middle-aged son. In 1980 Macra na Feirme began an advisory service to farming families who were interested in setting up farm partnerships. The scheme has been successful in helping hundreds of families solve the thorny problem of succession, and it is now administered by ACOT, the Council for the Development of Agriculture.

Farm Partnerships

A farm partnership is simply an agreement between two or more people running the farm (usually a parent and a successor), which sets out how work is to be managed between them, and how income is to be shared over the years. ACOT believes a family farm partnership offers the following advantages:

> A greater security for both partners.
>
> Both parents and successor enjoy the equal status of 'farm partners'.
>
> Parents can actively involve the successor without giving everything away.
>
> There is a blend of youth and experience in running the farm business.
>
> Stock and machinery transfer can be arranged over a period.
>
> A winding down of the farm business in line with the ageing of the farming family is prevented.

How to do it? The farm partnership is a written agreement with three main elements: (1) management, (2) profits and (3) ownership. Before the agreement is drawn up, partners have to sit down and discuss how decisions are arrived at, who has the final say, how profits are to be divided, how living expenses are to be decided, how the ownership is to be shared

and how it is to be transferred from father to heir. The key areas to be agreed upon include income sharing, management sharing, work sharing, property sharing, plus the duration, review and termination of the partnership. Accounting, borrowing and banking procedures, commitments to other family members, tax implications, housing arrangements, insurance and pension arrangements have all to be considered.

Very committed to the idea of partnership, ACOT has advisers all over the country helping many families to make the idea into a workable reality. ACOT also offers advice and help on a planned approach to succession, which involves the timely identification of a successor, and his gradual involvement in management and decision making. So progress on farm succession on retirement is happening in many individual cases. But a revised Voluntary Farm Retirement scheme at national level is still awaited, and probably should be reviewed in the context of a national pension plan. Any new farmers' scheme must ensure that the option of retirement provides a net benefit over competing state benefits for farmers who do not retire.

USEFUL CONTACTS AND REFERENCES

ACOT, Council for Development in Agriculture,
National Office,
Frascati, Blackrock,
Co Dublin.
Telephone: (01) 885361

Information and advice available on succession and farm partnerships.

ACOT branches at:

Castlebar, Telephone: (094) 21944
Cavan, Telephone: (049) 38257/31143
Clonmel, Telephone: (052) 21300
Donegal, Telephone: (074) 41133
Dundalk, Telephone: (042) 32263
Ennis, Telephone: (065) 21676
Fermoy, Telephone: (025) 32011
Galway City, Telephone: (091) 62101
Galway County, Telephone: (091) 44038
Kilkenny, Telephone: (056) 21153
Leitrim, Telephone: (078) 20028
Limerick, Telephone: (061) 45148
Longford, Telephone: (043) 6428
Cork East, Telephone: (021) 45489
Cork West, Telephone: (023) 45113
Monaghan, Telephone: (047) 81188
Mullingar, Telephone: (044) 40721
Naas, Telephone: (045) 79203
Navan, Telephone: (046) 21792
Nenagh, Telephone: (067) 31821
Piltown, Telephone: (051) 43105
Portlaoise, Telephone: (0502) 21326
Newcastle, Co Dublin, Telephone: (01) 288246
Roscommon, Telephone: (0903) 6166
Sligo, Telephone: (071) 2286
Tipperary, Telephone: (067) 31821
Tullamore, Telephone: (0506) 21405
Tullow, Telephone: (0503) 51210
Waterford, Telephone: (058) 41211
Tralee, Telephone: (066) 21077
Wexford, Telephone: (053) 22622
Wicklow, Telephone: (0404) 2315

Irish Farmer's Association,
Irish Farm Centre,
Bluebell, Dublin 12.
Telephone: (01) 501166

Macra na Feirme,
National Headquarters,
Irish Farm Centre,
Bluebell, Dublin 12
Telephone: (01) 501166

5. | What Are You Entitled To?

'Nothing is automatic in social welfare'; says Noel O'Sullivan, head of information with the National Social Service Board, the umbrella body running the 80 community information centres which tell people of their rights. He was referring specifically to the entitlement that most concerns people at retirement — their retirement pension. As explained in the last chapter, employers on retirement may pay a pension of up to two-thirds final salary. This total is made up partly by pension fund, partly by state pension, with the state contribution becoming increasingly important. For over 50% of workers retiring now, it may be all they have.

But many are discovering on retirement that they do not, in fact, qualify for a state retirement pension, despite up to 40 years at work. In order to explain why this occurs, we must look at the workings of the scheme, and its historical background. At first glance all is plain sailing. A state retirement pension is payable, irrespective of means, to an insured person who has reached the age of 65 and qualifies. This has not always been the case. Up to 1974 only those paying a social insurance contribution qualified for a state retirement pension. An insured person is the key phrase, and only the beginning of the necessary qualification. To qualify you must have a yearly average of at least 24 social insurance contributions from 1953 or the year you first paid

insurance (whichever is later). An average of 24 contributions entitles people to a minimum pension, 48 contributions are needed to get the maximum.

Calculating Your Eligibility

Eligibility is calculated by dividing the number of contributions (paid or credited) each year, by the number of years since entry into social insurance, or since 1953 (whichever is later), to arrive at an overall average. So, if you went to work in 1944, began stamping a card after the introduction of the Social Welfare Act of 1952 and paid contributions regularly throughout your working life, you can be sure of the maximum retirement pension when you leave work. You're probably equally safe if your income was over the insurable ceiling when you began working and didn't have to stamp a card for the first 30 years or so of your working life.

Bob who started working in 1944 came into the scheme in 1974 when the income ceiling was abolished, and every worker came under the social insurance net. When Bob retired this year, his record showed that he contributed continuously since 1974. He got a full pension. William Clarke has not been so lucky. In 1953 he was earning less than £600 a year, and had to stamp a card. Six months later he got promoted over the earnings ceiling, and didn't come into the social insurance net again until 1974, when, like everyone else, he began to pay his stamp.

William retired last year, confident of receiving a retirement pension. He needs it badly, as his occupational pension is quite small. But he does not qualify. When his social insurance record was examined, his average yearly stamp contribution from 1953 to retirement date was less than is needed to qualify, because he hadn't stamped a card for 20 years. William gets nothing, and it's not his fault. 'The system', says Noel O'Sullivan, 'is unfair. We hear heartbreaking stories regularly. Dozens of them. People are losing out through no fault of their own. They assume they will get a pension. They are totally shocked to discover they won't, and at this stage it is too late to do anything about it, because you cannot buy your way back in'.

What Categories Of Worker Are Most At Risk?

'The people who may feel most confident about receiving a state pension are those at either end of the scale', says Noel O'Sullivan. 'First, the man who entered the scheme in 1974, and who has a full record since and second, the lowly paid who were always stamping a card or getting credits. The person most at risk is the man who has come up in the world. The worker on the factory floor promoted to supervisor, middle management people, and those who were in and out of insurable employment in the fifties and sixties due to the earnings ceiling.

These would be the people who were stamping a card after 1953 in the early years of their working lives. Then they got a salary increase which put their income over the earnings ceiling and out of the scheme. They stopped stamping. They would have

had the option of staying in the scheme through voluntary contributions. But these were the years of high expenditure for them — buying a house, rearing a family, paying school fees. Few opted to contribute voluntarily, mainly because they didn't realise how important it could turn out to be years later. In the case of civil servants, public servants and army officers who don't qualify for a state pension themselves, their contributions to the widow's and orphan's fund contribute to a pension for their dependants. In some cases where they stopped paying, and did not become voluntary contributors, their widows have lost out years later'.

All these people came back into the net again in 1974 and would have a record until their retirement. But now at retirement, their early months or years of contribution are taken into account with any gaps when calculating their yearly average. The gaps bring the average down. In some cases they may qualify for a reduced pension, in others none at all. One of the worst cases Noel O'Sullivan has encountered is a man who had no stamps registered since 1951. He became ill in 1953 and fought successfully for three weeks sick benefit. This meant that his social insurance record began in 1953 with three credits, even though he didn't stamp again until 1974 when it became compulsory.

Retired now, he is regarded by official-dom as having been in the social insurance net since 1953, because of the three credits, and his yearly average is, therefore, way below the minimum for a pension. 'That few shillings in 1953 has cost him over £4,000 a year now in retirement pension', says Noel O'Sullivan. This situation was changed in 1986 — a record cannot start with a credit — and this man now enjoys a full Social Welfare Pension complete with arrears. So it is important while still at work to find out your eligibility for a state retirement pension. The best way to do so is to write to the Department of Social Welfare, Old Age Pension Section, D'Olier House, D'Olier Street, Dublin 2, quoting your PRSI number, and ask them if you will qualify. Their reply is a guidance and not a legal document.

What If You Don't Qualify For A Pension

People who do qualify for a retirement pension should apply for it three months before their sixty-fifth birthday. If you find you don't qualify, is there anything you can do? You could approach your firm, and see if they can improve your occupational pension to bridge the gap. 'Some do and some don't', says Noel, 'but it's worth asking'. Alternatively if you know you're going to have a shortfall in retirement, you could try and begin a system of additional voluntary contributions to improve your private pension fund, or take some of the other steps previously outlined to improve your financial position. You can take action only if you know your position in time.

Contributory Old Age Pension and Unemployment Benefit

A person who doesn't qualify for a retirement pension at 65, may still qualify for a contributory old age pension at 66 because the average yearly contributions needed are lower. For a contributory old age pension, you must have a yearly average of 20 registered (paid or credited) contributions between 1953 or the year you first started to pay insurance (whichever is later), and

the April before you reach 66. Keeping up the credits is achieved by signing on for work at the Employment Exchange between retirement and qualifying age. An average of 20 contributions gives the minimum pension, 48 gets the maximum. If you retire before the age of 65, you may qualify for unemployment benefit. The conditions are different from those for a retirement pension, and many who have been in continuous employment and paying PRSI will probably qualify. There are other conditions, however, related to work availablity. In order to receive unemployment benefit, you must sign on once a week at your local employment exchange, you must be capable and available for work and actively seeking work. Unemployment benefit normally lasts for 15 months, but if you are over 65 when that period ends, it may continue to be paid until you reach 66.

At 65 you may be eligible for either the retirement pension or unemployment benefit and take whatever is to your advantage. Unemployment benefit is not yet subject to income tax, while pensions are. Make an appointment with the local employment exchange, go down, and have your questions answered. Another irony of the system is that many retired people who do not qualify for a contributory pension due to insufficient stamps, can't get a non-contributory pension either, because their means are above the means test limit. 'Means are not just cash income', says Noel O'Sullivan, 'your house is not taken as means, but the value of property investments, or savings is counted. Many a man saves all his life, or invests his lump sum for extra income and finds he's over the earnings limit, and gets nothing.

The Poverty Trap

'It's called the poverty trap, and many people are caught in it. The reason is because of the way social welfare legislation has developed in this country. The old age pension didn't come into being until 1961, the retirement pension in 1970, PRSI in 1979, all comparatively recently. People today are being penalised for their actions in the fifties and sixties. It's really a shame, since many did not know or understand the consequences'. We referred earlier to the vulnerability of civil servants who went above the earnings ceiling, and didn't think of contributing voluntarily to the social welfare widow's and orphan's pension fund. Some of these men unwittingly left their wives very badly off. The contributory widow's pension is payable to a widow either on her own or her husband's social insurance record. There is no means test.

The woman who has been working full-time in the home during marriage is dependent on her husband's record for her entitlement. In some cases, because of the gap in contributions in the middle years, and failure to continue his record after early retirement, his yearly average is too low to qualify for her pension. She may qualify for a non-contributory widow's pension. But again, many men will have tried to make investment provisions for their wives, which puts them just above the non-contributory limit. Women in insurable employment qualify for the state widow's pension, retirement pension, and the contributory old age pension in their own right. The widow of a contributory old age pensioner is normally entitled to a full contributory widow's pension.

The final irony in the social welfare jungle, is that if you're inside, you may then be entitled to a further package of goodies. If you are left outside through the machinations of bureaucratic red tape, you are unlikely to qualify for a range of benefits, precisely at a time you may need them most. There are many allowances and benefits retired people should know about. Collectively they could make a huge difference to the quality of life in retirement.

Free Travel

Free travel on buses, coaches and trains is available to everyone aged 66 and over. This applies to CIE rail and road service, the Aran Islands Ferry Service, and certain private companies who have opted into the scheme. There is no reduction on the amount of travel, but journeys cannot be taken during peak morning and evening times. Eligible people receiving social welfare or health board payments normally get their travel passes automatically. Others can get application forms at the local post office, or from the Department of Social Welfare, 157 Townsend Street, Dublin 2. Telephone: (01) 717171.

Allowance for Elderly Single Women

An allowance, means tested, is paid to unmarried women between the ages of 58 and 66. Apply to Department of Social Welfare, 157/165 Townsend Street, Dublin 2. Telephone: (01) 717222.

Living Alone Allowance

This allowance is paid to people, married or single aged 66 or over, who receive some type of social welfare payment, and live entirely alone. Apply to the section of the Department of Social Welfare which pays your main pension or benefit.

Prescribed Relative Allowance

This one is paid to incapacitated people, over 66 who receive some type of pension from the Department of Social Welfare, and who need and receive full-time care from a relative. The relative must live with the person cared for, cannot have another job outside the home, or qualify for any other social welfare benefit. Apply to the Secretary of the Department of Social Welfare paying the main benefit. Married women are excluded.

Free Electricity Allowance

Up to 1,500 units of electricity a year are given to people over 66 on various social welfare pensions, to people who receive a British and Northern Ireland retirement pension; garda widows and people on invalidity pensions may also qualify. Application forms are available from the post office, and should be sent to the ESB or apply to the Department of Social Welfare, 157-164 Townsend Street, Dublin 2. Telephone: (01) 717171.

Free Bottled Gas Scheme

People not connected to the ESB system may qualify for the bottled gas equivalent of the electricity allowance. The place to apply to is the Bottled Gas Section of the Department of Social Welfare, 157-164 Townsend Street, Dublin 2. Telephone: (01) 717171.

Free Television Licence

Many people who qualify for the above two schemes also qualify for a free licence for a black and white television set. People with a colour set may meet the extra cost themselves. When applying, a recent ESB bill is proof of entitlement. Application forms are available at the post office, send to the Department of Social Welfare, 157-164 Townsend Street, Dublin 2. Telephone: (01) 717171.

Free Telephone Rental

Some people get free telephone rental though they have to pay for calls in the normal way. They include people who live alone, aged 66 and over and receive a social welfare pension, or a British social security pension, or a garda widows' pension. People of any age who live on an invalidity pension may also qualify. Applications to the Department of Social Welfare, 157-164 Townsend Street, Dublin 2. Telephone: (01) 717171.

Fuel Schemes

Many elderly people qualify for free or cheap fuel during winter. In some towns the scheme is operated by the local authority, and the fuel vouchers are given automatically with pension or allowance. People then go and buy the fuel themselves. These towns are Arklow, Balbriggan, Bray, Cork, Drogheda, Dublin, Dundalk, Enniscorthy, Gorey, Kilkenny, Limerick, New Ross, Waterford, Wexford and Wicklow. If there's a problem, apply to the local authority in those towns. Outside these areas, people should apply to the community welfare officer in the local health centre. If refused, appeals can be made to the chief executive officer of the health board. Local social service councils and the Society of St Vincent de Paul, plus other with fuel. Enquire at the nearest Community Information Centre or health centre. A new scheme will be in operation by the end of 1988.

Health Services

Many retired people qualify for a medical

card because of their drop in income. Medical cardholders are entitled to a range of health services, free of charge. These include doctors, drugs and hospital services. People with cards go to their GP in the normal way, and will be treated in the same way as fee-paying patients. Cardholders are entitled to certain prescribed drugs and medicines free of charge. They get free maintenance and free treatment in the public ward of a public hospital as well as free out-patient treatment. They may get free dental and optical treatment, hearing aids, and a range of other aids, like walking frames and other equipment, if the service is locally available.

Medical cardholders may be able to have their travel expenses to and from the doctor or hospital refunded by the local health board. Some of these perks, however, have been affected by health board cutbacks in certain areas. The place to apply for a medical card is the local health centre. They will explain the amount of income allowed each week within which people may qualify for a card. The limits are updated in January each year, but anyone with an income around the limit should still follow through their applications, particularly if they have heavy medical expenses, or heating needs, because each case is examined on its merits.

People on a social security pension from an EEC country, not Ireland, are entitled to a medical card regardless of means. This entitlement is an EEC regulation. If however, they have earned income, social welfare or social welfare pension paid in Ireland, they lose this entitlement. There is a middle group who won't qualify for a medical card, but may receive a hospital services card. Well worth applying for, this card gives free maintenance and treatment in a public hospital ward, and free outpatient services. Some categories of people who have made voluntary contributions in the seventies to social insurance may also qualify. The 1987 £10 hospital charges apply.

Dental and Optical Benefits

Also, the Department of Social Welfare provide dental and optical benefits, and help with hearing aid costs to insured workers who have enough insurance contributions. And a worker who is entitled to these benefits at 65 or 66 retains the entitlement for life. Treatment is provided by private dentist and optician. Apply to the Department of Social Welfare, 157-164 Townsend Street, Dublin 2. Telephone: (01) 717171, or nearest health board. Medical and surgical aids and appliances are usually free of charge to hospital service cardholders, if they are part of hospital treatment. Even if not, the health board may contribute to their cost, if asked. For information, contact the National Rehabilitation Board, 25 Clyde Road, Dublin 4. Telephone: (01) 684181.

But everyone, irrespective of income, is entitled to something free; maintenance in a public ward of a public hospital, free outpatient service, excluding consultant's fees, if applicable. People without cards must pay for the treatment in a public ward in a public hospital, and for any consultant's fees involved in outpatient work. Everyone is entitled to a refund on drugs and medicines over a certain figure paid out in one month. This can be reclaimed from the health board, the chemist has the necessary receipts and claim forms, and they must be sent in to the local health board at the end of each month.

Other Services You Should Know About

Nursing: All the health boards employ public health nurses who have the care of elderly people as one of their main duties. The services of the nurse are normally free of charge to all people over 65, and all medical cardholders. Nurses will bath someone who cannot manage this alone, change dressings, ensure that the person is eating properly and not suffering from anaemia, and generally act as a channel to other local services; doctor, social worker, home help, dentist. Anyone who would like the public health nurse to call should contact their local health centre, or family doctor.

Home Helps: Many areas have home helps; pleasant, efficient people who help others, particularly elderly people, in their own homes. The aim is to help people with the chores they can't do themselves, rather than do them for them. Help is given with jobs such as hoovering, dusting, bed-making, general housework, shopping. In many cases a relationship is established, which is a very welcome spin-off. Like many community initiatives, the aim of the home help service is to keep elderly people out in the community, and to provide the necessary support to make this possible.

The service is means tested, but not linked solely to ability to pay. People are referred by nurses, doctors, social workers and caring neighbours. The availability of the scheme varies greatly between health board areas. Contact the home help organiser of the local health centre for more local information.

Social Workers: All health boards employ social workers, who can advise elderly people on the range of services available to them locally, while also providing advice, support and guidance on specific family or personal problems. Availability of social workers varies from region to region. Ask at the local health centre, surgery, social service centre or community information centre.

The Following Services May Also Be Available In Your Area

Meals on Wheels: Now fairly widely available, this service offers a hot, cooked meal three or four times a week to individuals or couples not easily able to cater properly for themselves every day. Means tested, again this service is not narrowly administered, and relies heavily on local voluntary effort to cook and deliver the food.

Laundry Service: This may be provided by a local voluntary organisation, and the local health centre is the place to ask.

Chiropody Service: This is sometimes provided by health boards free of charge to medical cardholders over 65. Many social service councils provide a similar service, and may charge a small fee. Application for these services in all cases is at the local health centre, social service council or community information centre.

If in Doubt, Apply

The golden rule about entitlements is: 'if in doubt, apply'. The take-up rate on many free benefits is low, mainly because people either don't know that a particular service exists, or doubt their entitlement to it. So, if in doubt, apply. There is a school of thought that says getting a load of free hand-outs is degrading to the receiver. Some people, entitled to a range of services, choose not to apply and manage well without them. This is their right. Equally other people don't want the agencies of the state to know their business, and refuse to have their financial affairs examined to determine means. Equally fine. But it seems a shame that very many people in real need don't get, say, a hearing aid or a hot meal regularly, when both are available, simply because they don't know how to apply.

For these people a local helping hand is available in community information centres around the country. Here trained staff will either know or find out your entitlement. They will certainly know where and how to apply, will have many of the application and claim forms at the ready and will assist in filling them in if needed. Today there are about 80 such centres in cities and towns around Ireland. They offer a very comprehensive information and advice service to everyone free. They're experts on topics such as social welfare and health entitlements, problems with pension, unemployment, redundancy and more. Centres are staffed by trained volunteers. They are not all open all day — some open in the evening. To find out where your nearest community information centre is, contact the National Social Service Board, 71 Lower Leeson Street, Dublin 2. Telephone: (01) 616422, for a complete list.

Other Benefits:

As well as a package of statutory entitlements, elderly people are wooed from home by another bundle of discounts and concess-ions. Here is a brief cross-section on what is available:

Indoor: Many cinemas around the country offer price reductions to people on an old age pension. Typically tickets may be bought at half price, or less, though some establishments confine concessions to afternoon performances only. In Dublin, the National Concert Hall welcomes people on old age pensions at half-price to all symphony concerts, Telephone: (01) 711888. The Gate Theatre, Cavendish Row gives free tickets on Monday nights if seats are available. Check beforehand, phone (01) 744045. Also, old age pensioners are allowed in free into Dublin Corporation swimming pools.

Outdoor: Admission to many ancestral homes and gardens around the country is at a reduced rate to people on an old age pension. Dublin Zoo is free to all pensioners, as is entry to the RDS, Ballsbridge's lunchtime and evening concerts and lectures. (Contact them for their calendar of events, by letter or phone (01) 680645). There is no charge either for entry to the Spring show and Horse Show, or to lectures and recitals during winter. A day at the races may be free to pensioners too. Establishments differ, best phone and check and see what local arrangements there are.

Services: Allied Irish Banks (AIB) offer free banking on current accounts and cashsave accounts for the over 65s, providing the account is kept in credit.

Bank of Ireland 'Golden Years' package for people over 60, offers free current accounts whether debit or credit. There is no charge for transaction, cheque card, bank drafts or gift cheques. They offer a free advisory service on tax, wills and inheritances, and the monthly income savings accounts and travellers cheques issued are free of commission.

Northern Bank offer free banking if your account is in credit.

Ulster Bank give free banking to people over 60 whose accounts are in credit also free travellers cheques, gift cheques and bank drafts.

Many dry cleaning firms throughout the country offer 50% off normal charges to people on pension if they come in on Tuesday morning. Similarly, hairdressing salons around the country offer half or reduced price service to older people early in the week. Check locally. There are an assortment of other reductions from firms, sporting organisations, and places of entertainment up and down the country. The best advice is to check before you go, or as you arrive. Always carry your CIE pass or pension book with you, ready to whip out on cue. And remember, always ask if there is a reduction or concession — there often will be. You'll never know if you don't ask, and by posing the question have everything to gain, and nothing to lose.

USEFUL CONTACTS AND REFERENCES

Summary of Social Insurance and Social Assistance, a book which gives conditions for eligibility and how to apply.

The Rates Book
Checklist for Pensions,
Pensioners and Savings
up to date rates of all benefits, published every year, and available free from:

The Department of Social Welfare,
Information Section,
Store Street,
Dublin 1.
Telephone: (01) 786466

Entitlements for the Elderly
published each July by:

National Social Service Board,
71 Lr Leeson Street,
Dublin 2.
Telephone: (01) 616422

Social service organisations and/or community information centres may be found in the following places:

Dublin:
Ballymun, Blackrock, Blanchardstown, Cabra West, Coolock, Clontarf, Crumlin, Dalkey, Donnycarney, Dun Laoire, Finglas, Gardiner Street, Inchicore, Killester, Liberties, Lucan, Malahide, Mt. Argus, North Wall, Raheny, Rialto, Palmerstown, Stillorgan, Skerries, Sallynoggin, Whitehall, Westland Row, Whitefriar Street.

Around the Country:
Abbeyleix, Ardee, Arklow, Athenry, Athlone, Ballina, Ballinrobe, Bishopstown, Bantry, Blackpool (Cork), Blackrock (Cork), Buncrana, Boyle, Bray, Carlow, Cashel, Castlebar, Claremorris, Clonmel, Cork, Cobh, Drogheda, Dunboyne, Dundalk, Dungarvan, Carrickmacross, Ennis, Enniscorthy, Freshford, Galway, Gorey, Kilkenny, Kilrush, Killarney, Kiltimagh, Letterkenny, Limerick, Longford, Loughrea, Mallow, Mullingar, Nenagh, Newbridge, Naas, Mayfield (Cork), Roscrea, Shannon, Sligo, Stradbally, Skibereen, Thurles, Tipperary, Togher, Tuam, Tramore, Wexford.

6.

Where Will You Live?

Patricia and John Dargan sold their family home and moved into an apartment the year they retired. Looking back now, adding up the pros and cons, they feel they're ahead on points. They've gained financially. The price they got for their home paid for the apartment, with enough over for a tidy nest egg. They have invested this to give regular income and some capital growth. They've gained long-term with a new home that is small enough for two, easy to keep and maintain. They've lost out on space and large chunks of the family can't come and stay as easily as before. They've lost their much-loved garden, and they're still adjusting to a labour-saving lifestyle which gives more time to fill each day.

Moving house in retirement can be a tricky business, and most couples probably gain and lose in the exchange. In the Dargan's case, it wasn't a hasty decision. 'We thought long and hard about the move before we decided', said Patricia, 'we didn't want to move away from the area where we have lots of friends. But the house had got too big for just the two of us, and we needed extra income. John's pension is quite small. Selling the house and using some of the money to buy an apartment while invest-

ing the rest, seemed to solve a lot of our problems, so that's what we did.'

A Great Adventure

They bought the show flat in a new apartment block less than a mile away from their old home. Bright, compact and nicely decorated, it has a large living/dining area, small kitchen, and two bedrooms. Furnishing a new house again was a great adventure. 'We had great fun choosing everything', said John, 'and, as you can see, we went for light cane furniture because we thought it suited the place best. We got rid of a lot of the old pieces we've had for years.' They didn't feel sentimental at parting with these, but their ornaments and photographs were a different matter. John has built several shelves for these in the living area, and they transform the apartment into a home.

Long-term, they feel the move will be beneficial. The apartment is warm, easy to keep. They feel secure, and a maintenance contract ensures that the exterior will be landscaped and regularly painted. They have adjusted well to less space. Six foldaway chairs are produced when friends or family visit. The dining table has long

44

drop-leaf sides and folds away when not in use. They bought a nest of tables for their own meals by the electric log fire. They may not hang out washing, and drape it on a special line over the bath.

There are drawbacks to the streamlined days. 'Time hangs a bit heavy', said John, 'and we could do with something for a few hours each day'. They take a walk each morning, visit family and friends regularly, they're frequent day-trippers on DART which passes the door. They also take advantage of reduced afternoon cinema admissions, and both are great readers. 'But you can't be going to the pictures, or on the train every day,' says John, 'we do need something'. Both would like a part-time job, or morning class to provide separate stimulation and interest, because even the most devoted couple can have too much togetherness. . . 'we do everything together, really,' says Patricia, 'and we get on very well, almost all the time'.

Now It's Our Time

'We sometimes rub up against each other the wrong way', says John, 'we're both good cooks. I'm very fussy in the kitchen, and I can disapprove of the way Patricia organises herself. We've learnt from experience that when one cooks, the other stays out of the kitchen and does the washing up afterwards.' The couple have five children, all now left home. 'We discussed the move fully with them', said Patricia, 'they encouraged us, but I don't think they realised what it would mean. I have a married daughter living abroad, and a son also abroad. They came back last year, expected to stay with us, and were taken aback that they couldn't because there wasn't the space'. But the parents have no

regrets on that score. 'We gave them all the time they needed when they were growing up — now it's our time — we love to see the grandchildren coming, but we love to see them going as well'.

The reasons for John and Patricia's move were financial, but there are other considerations when planning ahead. Pamela is a single woman living on in the family home which she now admits is too big and expensive to heat and maintain. The house that suited while the family was being reared may not be right now that most members are gone. It may indeed be too big, too difficult or expensive to run, to keep warm. In considering the suitability of your present home, these are the questions to ask:

It's been your home for years and still suitable at 65. How right will it be when you're 75 or 80?

What kind of repair is it in? Are there expensive jobs that need doing? Is there damp, rot, woodworm, bad wiring or a faulty roof? Can you afford major work?

Has it got too big? Do you tend to use only three or four rooms? How much time is spent in housework, time that could be spent more enjoyably?

How well do you manage the garden now? How well will it fare in five years time? In ten?

Do you have stairs?, are they a problem? Is your home built on a hill? The ground you cover at 65 may make you breathless at 70.

How accessible are you to shops, buses, doctor, church, post office?

Moving to a New Area

A house that becomes too large and difficult could become a growing burden. A garden that was a delight for its flowers and lawns, and a source of satisfaction with fruit and vegetables, may become a source of frustration, anxiety and overwork. Local accessibility is also important. The older people get, the more a sense of isolation can grow if local amenities are not within walking or driving distance, or on a good bus route. In moving, there are two choices — first a completely new start in a new area and second, a more suitable home in the same neighbourhood.

Fred and Jean Kavanagh emigrated to London in the 1940s, retired and moved rather hastily back to Ireland ten years ago. They bought a pleasant seaside bungalow in the south-east at a bargain price. He had always wanted to come home, she didn't feel the pull, enjoyed her job, London shops, theatre and bustle. The move has not been an unqualified success. 'I nearly went out of my mind during the first six months', Jean admits. 'I couldn't get used to the silence. I can only describe this place as a one-horse town, beautiful to look at, but nothing to do'.

Fred settled in quickly and well. He has the kind of chatty, outgoing personality that makes friends easily, and he is now very involved in the town. He goes out four nights a week to cards, bingo, old folk's socials. Jean does none of this. She doesn't socialise at all, but keeps herself busy with cooking, knitting and housework, and after ten years, still looks back nostalgically to her London days. Both are critical of Irish life, the high cost of living, and poor standards of workmanship.

The Out-Of-Season Test

So if you're moving to a completely new area, do your homework first. Will it suit you? What are its facilities like? Are there local shops to avoid long treks with shopping bags? Is there a library, any day classes, any clubs catering for your interest, whether it be bridge, gardening or scuba diving? What's the bus service like? If you have free travel, it's a shame not to use it. Our world becomes more localised when we retire, and the amenities on our doorstep can make a big difference to the kind of life we can enjoy. Imagine what the place would be like on a wet November Tuesday, or a freezing day in February. Still viable?

Many people (and this applies to Britain more than Ireland) dream of retiring to the coast, to the sunny south-east, forgetting that it becomes the cold, wet south-east from November to March each year. So do the out-of-season test. If you have spent a fortnight every summer in a balmy village in Kerry or Connemara, and seriously consider retiring there, go and stay in spring, autumn and winter, and see if you still love it as much. Consider what you're leaving behind. A new place will be an adventure, but will also take you away from the familiar — friends, neighbours, local walks, shops.

The move may be of greater significance to the full-time housewife, rather than her husband who has made so much of his life outside the home anyway. Women must speak out, and share fully how they would feel about any proposed uprooting. Single people should realise that they may feel lonely until they make friends. Will the new place be more difficult for family and friends to come and visit, and you them? Family links seems to become even more important in retirement, when there is more time. Make sure a move wouldn't cut you off from what could be a source of continuing pleasure and affection.

Your House: When you retire your home ceases to be just the place to come home to, it becomes the headquarters, the office, the social centre. Home-based people need space to live in harmony. So don't go for somewhere too small, you may be glad of an extra room to listen to music, sew, sulk, read the paper or see a friend. Obviously, you're moving to get away from some of the imperfections of the old, so be critical of the new — its state of repair, heating, kitchen layout. How easy will it be to heat,

47

clean, maintain? Buying a small house will probably mean selling furniture you've had for years. Are you prepared for this emotionally and financially?

Pick a sunny location. Note where the sun comes in. Is there a room that gets the sun all day, and could this become the den, saving on heating bills, and adding to the pleasantness of each day? Unless you hate gardening, do have a little garden too. Gardeners talk about the deep satisfaction of planting, feeding and seeing things grow. This pleasure can be all the keener when the childbearing years are over. People still wish to be involved in nurturing life, it just fills a need we all have. On a less lofty note, your garden is a lovely place to sit on a warm May day thinking of all the pour souls still slaving away in a dusty office block:

The Cost of Moving House

Moving house costs money and a lot of the profit made in changing from the bigger to a small establishment could be swallowed up with legal costs, auctioneering fees, advertising, transport charges, equipping and decoration. People should get an accurate idea of the legal costs from the beginning. You should realistically assess the furnishing bill. If you haven't bought carpets, curtains or furniture for 30 years, you will be taken aback at the price tags. When furnishing a small area, remember a plain carpet will give a feeling of space and unity, with colour patterns being picked up from curtains, upholstery, bed linen. One tip — put the blankets away, and buy a feather duvet quilt. It will keep you just as cosy, and make bed-making a painless affair.

Granny Flats: As time goes on, many retired people are forced to give up the independence of their own home in exchange for the security and comfort of living with relatives.

This can be a great success or a great failure. Bridget Lee went to live with her married daughter Catherine two years ago, and the arrangement has worked out splendidly with an increase of affection, friendship and cooperation all round. Nellie Corcoran moved from England to live with her married daughter Karen, but now four years later, their home is not a happy place.

The difference between the two is planning, or lack of it. Nellie and Karen do not have compatible personalities, mother is precise, daughter slapdash. They get on each other's nerves, each feeling resentful and frustrated. With a bit of thought on both sides, this could have been realised, and the decision to live together cancelled. Or they could have drawn up a specific plan to express the differences, and try and meet both women's needs.

Bridget's daughter Catherine is a doctor, with a local practice. Bridget fell ill, and was no longer able to look after herself properly. The family invited her to come and share their home. Bridget herself paid for the garage conversion, and they had an architect draw up plans incorporating her wishes. Her new home is charming. Formerly a dumping ground for bikes and paraphernalia, the garage, measuring 9ft x 12ft has been converted into a modern, self-contained bed-sitter. The entrance is a door set into an attractive timber framed wall, across which Bridget draws the curtains at night. To her immediate left she has sink unit, fridge, two hot hobs, shelves and cupboard for delph and provisions, with a worktop at the correct height for her to chop her vegetables without getting a pain in her back.

The right hand wall has an electric coal fire, a television set, nest of tables, book shelves, and closed cupboad containing clothes, cosmetics and toiletries. To the left is her bed, hidden from public view by a half-wall. Beside the bed, a locker, above, a shelf for books and ornaments. Built under the bed are two drawers with out-of-season clothes and bed linen. She has two easy chairs in the centre of the room. Bridget's back door leads directly to her own bathroom, toilet and washroom. She has direct access to the back garden, a huge source of pleasure to her. 'I love gardening. I feel the sap rising within me each spring, and I'm mad to be out in the garden'.

Rules

Bridget is 73 now, and was initially reluctant about the move. 'I thought it would be too close to the main family and the children'. So before she moved in, she sat down with the family, and they jointly decided on a few rules.

'I said that when I was feeling well, I would babysit for them, but not if they were going to be extremely late. Also that they were not to expect me to come in and sit with the family in the evening as they need their own time together'. Catherine, for her part, said the children had to knock on Bridget's door and ask permission to enter. She was at liberty to say 'yes' or 'no'. Bridget's official duties are to clean out the fire in the house in the morning, and babysit on Monday night.

Unofficially she's there most afternoons when the youngest comes in from school. They have established the routine, he has coffee and a biscuit with granny, and he's now beating her at draughts. Unofficially, she does a lot of the gardening, because she has the most interest in it. Unofficially, she will give the house a little tidy if it needs it, and sometimes she will prepare vegetables for the main family meal. She cooks for herself every day, and comes to the family for Sunday lunch. She goes shopping with Catherine on Friday and buys what she wants for the week. Bridget's unwritten rules to herself include the following: Never interfere between wife and husband, and never invite confidences from one side about the other. Never interfere in the rearing of the children.

A Satisfactory Arrangement

Her verdict is that the arrangement has worked well. She feels safe and secure. She lives rent-free, but pays for her own food, electricity and heating. She is involved with the family, she has her garden. She is near her daughter whom she loves deeply, and she gets the best of medical attention from her. When she's not feeling well, she shuts the door, keeps to herself and goes to bed. Having granny with them, means the loss of a side entrance. The children have to take their bikes through the house, and they've built a shed in the back garden to house bikes and other equipment.

The arrangement has been just as satisfactory for Catherine. 'During the early years of my marriage, I rather kept mama at bay while I concentrated on my career. I suppose I was a bit on the defensive. I used to rush down and see her and rush away again, I usually had the children with me, and she used to say, ''I never get to see you on your own.'' We had become a little estranged, so when I invited my mother to come and live with me, we didn't know how it would work out. She made the most important rule of all, that she wouldn't be with us in the evenings. We started off as we meant to go on. I remember mama was here a few months, and I asked my husband one night if we should invite her in. He said, ''no, I think she values her independence as much as we do ours''.

'It has all worked out better than I had ever thought. Now I don't worry about her, I know how she is. We've continued to be honest. Sometimes I come home and she's exhausted, and I find she's been skivvying in the house, and I'm inclined to say, ''it's your own fault, nobody asked you to do it.'' There was another problem I worried about. As an only child, she thinks the sun and moon shine out of me. I can do no wrong, which puts a huge pressure on me to live up to that image. For the first few weeks, I was on my best behaviour, all sweetness and light to everyone. But of course, I couldn't keep that up, and one day, roared at everyone, and realised the great relief of continuing to be able to be myself. The children love having her here, and I think it has given them an extra dimension. They each have a relationship with her, and it's very important to them'.

A Home within a Home

Living with relatives can work, even if the house does not lend itself to separate establishments. At 74, Vera Colebrook was fitted with a heart pacemaker, suffered from angina, and could no longer live alone. Her niece and nephew-in-law in Stillorgan, Dublin invited her to come and live with them, and she accepted. I met her five years later. 'There hasn't been a cross word in all that time', she said 'the secret of our

success is good manners, consideration, and an awareness of everyone's need for privacy, for their own piece of territory'. Vera's home within a home was a small ground floor bed-sitting room, with the family bathroom and kitchen nearby. She lived surrounded by her own books, television set and photographs. She entertained her own friends, and had complete control of her day.

'The family leaves a tray for me each evening so I make my own continental breakfast here in my own time in the morning. I do the washing up for the whole family during the morning, leaving my niece a clean kitchen when she comes in. I get my own lunch, something light and easy. I usually have to take a rest in the afternoon. The family gives me my dinner on a tray, and I have it here on my own. I join them for the Sunday meal, for birthdays and celebrations. I am frequently asked to join them if they have friends in for the evening, but I usually refuse. I have a bell by my bed, and can ring it during the night if I need to, or if they don't hear me moving around in the day, they may come and knock to make sure I'm all right. Occasionally I will have to spend one whole day in bed, but they don't fuss me — they allow me to make my own decisions about how I feel.'

'I decided not to expect or let anyone do anything for me that I could do myself, and when I moved into the family, I vowed not to take from their lives, but to add to them in any way I could. She said it had been a beautiful five years, with mutual affection and friendship as its base. 'It has opened up a whole new world. One of my grand-nephews is in a group, and now I know all about gigs, I watch *Top of the Pops*, something I didn't watch before. I have been so much better physically, because all the fear of living alone, or having a heart attack with nobody there, is gone'.

Rules of Relativity

Vera died at 80. But her ten 'Rules of Relativity' live on and should be pinned on the wall of any family interested in peaceful co-existence. I reprint them here with her family's permission:

---

1. Don't hang on to your independence too long. Move into the family while still in full possession of your senses, don't wait until you have to be helped over the threshold in your senility.

2. Be sure in advance there is room for you. Never allow one of the children give up a room for you.

3. Recognise from the start that your daughter, daughter-in-law or niece, is the mistress of the house, you aren't. She has the right to run it her way, not your's. So don't offer unsought advice, don't interfere, don't criticise. Above all, never criticise her children. Bite into your gums if you have to, but keep your mouth shut.

4. You are now a permanent member of the household. Don't potter at the heels of others asking if you can help. By arrangement, make yourself responsible for set chores, then do them at the agreed time.

5. So far as possible, have your meals in your own room. Family mealtimes are usually times for family affairs. Besides, nothing is more off-putting to others at the table, than to have to listen to the champing of false teeth, and by now you've probably got tnem.

6. Strictly control your inquisitiveness. A nosey old person is a bane, and the less you ask, the more you're likely to be told.

7. Don't natter on and on about nothing. Conversation and amusing companionship aren't always synonymous.

8. Don't air your views as if they were God-given. Your prejudices have probably hardened with your arteries.

9. Avoid personal archeology, don't keep on digging up your past.

10. Allow the family to entertain their friends without you. Don't automatically sit in every time, or assume you are included in every family invitation.

Retirement Complexes

Ballygihen Apartments, Sandycove, Co Dublin opened in 1985. The complex consists of sixteen self-contained homes and a communal living area. It is administered by a resident secretary, Creina Foley, who has experience of such retirement complexes in Britain. She believes the Ballygihen advantage is that it gives retired people security plus independence, and a sense of community, in so far as they wish it.

Security provision includes secure locks on all doors and windows, one entry only to each apartment and the complex floodlit each night. The outer gate is locked and is accessible only to residents and friends through a special key. Each apartment has a telephone, allowing callers to be monitored and each apartment is linked to a central control, so there is constant contact and coverage.

"A lot of residents talk about the great feeling of safety since they came here" says Miss Foley, "many came from homes where they were burgled. One of our residents used to go to bed regularly with a golf stick at the ready, she says since she has moved here, she has relaxed completely and feels very secure''.

Residents range in age from mid-sixties upwards, there is a mix of married couples and people living alone: ''People's independence is respected totally'' says Miss Foley, ''we come and go as we please, people have friends in, family and grandchildren visit. There is friendship between residents, and privacy too''.

There is also a ready-made community for those who want it. Morning coffee is served in the pleasant communal sitting room several mornings a week, but the most popular shared cuppa is afternoon tea on the sunny patio during the summer months: ''We follow the sun around throughout the day'' says Creina Foley.

While apartments are suited to those physically and mentally well and alert, Creina Foley takes her role seriously, and if a resident is unwell, she offers support, practical help, and liaison with family and doctor as required.

The homes are compact and attractive. They are sold carpeted throughout, but unfurnished, except for some built-in fixtures. The double front door gives way to a square living area, graced by an elegant marble fireplace.

The kitchen is tiny but fully equipped with oven, hob, fridge, washing machine, waste disposal unit, extractor fan, floor and wall cupboards. The bedroom has two built-in wardrobes, and the bathroom has bath, toilet and roomy shower, often more suitable for older people than negotiating a slippery bath. The two-bedroomed apartments have an extra bathroom.

Little touches for the older person include plugs at waist rather than floor level, and a cord in the bathroom which if pulled rings an alarm in central office. Heating is provided by electric central heating, supplemented by storage heaters.

The complex offers secure parking, a small lockup area for each resident and a communal washing machine for people who don't want to be disturbed by the whir and splash in their own little kitchen.

Creina Foley feels that people considering apartment living must make some particular decisions: ''A lot of people are put off because they can't bring all their furniture, there just isn't room. So if a couple, or a person, feel they must have all their possessions around them, this way of life is not for them.

However if you opt for safety, community and independence, this works out very well indeed. It's a question of making choices, and deciding on your own priorities''.

She also believes retirement complexes should be situated in the heart of a bustling environment: ''It's no use building retirement apartments away from everything, cut off from life, people get quickly isolated, and that's not healthy.''

Staying in a familiar area is also important. Most of her residents have lived most of their lives in south Dublin and they are still within reachable distance of family, friends, church and social amenities.

The price of a two-bedroomed apartment is £55,000, one bedroomed apartments cost £48,000, and there is space for more building. Residents also pay an annual charge of £1,200 to cover security, maintenance and gardener. The plots outside each house are immaculate, though some enthusiasts insist on doing their own.

Sheltered Housing: Ballygihen is a private complex, but the sheltered housing idea for the over-60s has been gaining ground generally among health boards for some years, and today there are over 50 such schemes in the country housing a total of about 4,000 people. In most cases, the scheme represents cooperation between the local authority who build and maintain the flats, and the local health board who pays for staffing. One of the oldest complexes and still a good model is Rochestown House, Dun Laoghaire. Built in 1972, the house has 34 flats — eight doubles, and 26 singles. Each flat is self-contained. Occupants pay the same rate of local authority rent that they would normally pay, operated on a differential scale, according to means.

People come and go as they please, do their own shopping, see family and friends, invite them round for a meal, choose their hobbies. There are fringe benefits. There is a hot meal going in the communal dining room every weekday for those that want it. Most do. There is a resident caretaker couple who are on constant call. A doctor and nurse visit regularly. If you're sick, your meal will be brought to your flat. If it's too cold or too slippy to get out and do the messages or collect the pension, the caretaker will do that chore for you. People must be 60 to qualify for a place in the house, and the age range is from 60 to 80. Visiting, I got the impression that people can be as private or as matey as they choose.

Waiting Lists

I met one woman who never eats in the dining room, she has always cooked for herself and her husband, and continues to do so even after 13 years at Rochestown House. For her the benefits are a warm, pleasant place to live at a relatively modest rent. Others participate more in the communal life of the house, in visiting and outings. Rochestown House was built for £140,000, a snip by today's standards. The local authority agree it is a most cost-effective way of keeping elderly people out in the community. It combines dignity and independence, with back-up support. Most of the sheltered schemes have waiting lists, and applications are taken on the basis of need. Many of the people who qualify will have been living in damp, old flats, or been evicted, or fallen ill and been unable to look after themselves on their own. New imaginative housing ideas for elderly people are being discovered all the time. For example, in the west of Ireland over 150 elderly people are being fostered out with friends and neighbours. The care-givers receive a standard payment, made up of a contribution from the local health board and one from the elderly person. This is a scheme more health boards could investigate. It has the advantage of keeping someone who can no longer look after themselves out of hospital and in the community. They live with a family, which they usually enjoy, and it is a very cost-effective scheme, costing far less than hospitalisation.

Staying Put: But having looked at some of the housing options in retirement, it must be said that most retiring people stay put, at least initially. They don't move, but stay in the family home they've lived in for years. '. . .We made friends on the road when our children were small, we have all our friends and neighbours here, we couldn't move now.'

'. . .I wouldn't move and leave my

garden and all the changes we've made in the house over the years'.

'. . .Too expensive, it costs too much to move these days', are some of the opinions I've heard.

It was notable that most women dwelt on the emotional advantages, the link with neighbours, the garden. Men considered the practical aspects, the costs; so wives and husbands look on the question slightly differently. Staying put may mean making changes for the better. When we live in a place for a long time, we get used to its foibles and imperfections. We automatically give the sticking-back door an extra tug, and prop up the unsteady table leg with the old dictionary.

Home Improvements

At retirement, there is probably much we can do to make our homes more comfortable, more accident and burglar proof. In compiling a check list, it is a good idea to separate the plan into (a) jobs needing more money than time, and (b) jobs needing more time than money. The first may have to be done professionally, a

DIY approach will suffice for the second. Have the big jobs done before you retire. Don't use precious pension in large capital outlay. Do it now, rather than later, and here is a cross-section of typical jobs, gleaned for retirement people:

Big Jobs: Insulate — consider cavity wall insulation, attic insulation, double glazing.

Convert — perhaps an extra toilet downstairs, for someone with bad arthritis or a heart condition.

Replace faulty equipment. Why not scrap the twin tub that floods the kitchen every time, and get an automatic that makes the job much easier?

Consider change of heating. Older people think there's nothing like an open fire, and they're right. But open fires can be dangerous, people fall into them, burn themselves taking out hot ashes, slip bearing home briquettes, fall on ice fetching in coal.

Investigate heating alternatives. Many retired people are installing switch-on artificial coal; heat, cosy, clean and minimum maintenance.

Perhaps put a carpet in the bathroom now that the children aren't there to make waves, also consider a fitted staircarpet that does away with dusting and deadens noise.

Think about changing from soft, low chairs offering little support to something firmer, higher and easier to get in and out of.

When it comes to home repair and maintenance, beware of the dishonest tradesman. Retired people have told me many sad stories about guarantees not subsequently being honoured when things went wrong and poor workmanship over which they had no comeback. There are trade associations now covering most trades so, before you hire someone, try and discover how reputable he is. A list of trade associations is obtainable through the golden pages of the telephone directory.

Best of all, use someone who has been personally recommended to you by someone you know and trust. Consult your Community Information Centre about your rights in the matter of services. Get an estimate in writing of how much the work will cost, and withhold some payment until the job has been done to your satisfaction. There are many small jobs you can do yourself. In no particular order, you can buy and fit draught stripping to insulate windows and doors to keep in the heat you have. You can replace damaged mats with new ones, replace dim lights with brighter. If you don't already own one, consider buying an electric blanket for cold nights.

Accident Prevention: Every year several hundred elderly people die in Ireland at home as a result of falls, by far the most common cause of death. Next is accidental poisoning by drugs, then suffocation by inhaling gas vapour, then burning from fire or hot substances. There are no figures available on the number of serious accidents to retired people at home. A canvas of medical opinion, however, confirms that thousands are seriously injured every year, mainly through falls, secondly through burns, scalds and fire damage. It's not that we get stupid and decrepit in old age, but physically we slow up, our joints may get stiffer, our reactions slower, accidents happen. . . So there is a lot you can do to make your home safe. Use the following as a check list:

Moving About Safely:
Are doorways, halls, passages, stairs and landing well lit and free from clutter?

Are floors, steps and outside paths in good repair and free of uneven or slippery patches?

Are carpets, rugs, mats and lino in good repair, without tears, wrinkles and with non-slip backing?

Is your home free from trailing electric flexes and cables?

Are your shoes and slippers in good repair?

Do you know how to get out quickly in the event of a fire?

Have you a bedside lamp or torch handy at night?

Have you had your eyes tested recently?

Reaching Safely:
Are shelves and cupboards in daily use within easy reach?

Can you open and clean windows without strain?

Are door handles, plugs, light switches and gas supply taps easy to use without too much bending or reaching?

Can you store fuel near enough to avoid cold and strain in the winter?

Keeping Warm Safely:
Are fires and heaters in good repair and well guarded?

Do you use a fire guard with an open fire?

Do you keep portable heaters well clear of furniture and out of people's way?

Do you store paraffin and bottle gas safely?

Do you have the chimney swept once a year?

Switching on Safely:
Are your electrical appliances, flexes, plugs and power points in a good state of repair?

Are all plugs properly wired and fused?

55

Do you take care not to overload power points by plugging several appliances into an unfused adaptor?

Do you ensure that flexes don't trail across hot or wet surfaces, nor appliances handled with wet hands?

Does your kettle switch off automatically when boiled?

Do you keep your electric blanket dry, flat and serviced regularly?

At bedtime, do you switch off and unplug all appliances?

Cooking Safely:
Is your kitchen safe to work in with well-placed surfaces beside cooker and sink?

Are your worktops and cupboards the right height for you?

Is your gas cooker placed so that a sudden draught doesn't blow out the flame?

Do you keep saucepan handles clear of lighted burners and hot plates?

Have you a small wall fire-extinguisher?

Do you keep a first aid kit handy?

Safety in Rooms:
Are your rooms well ventilated?

If you smoke, have you enough deep ashtrays?

Do you appreciate the dangers of smoking in bed?

If you still use hot water bottles, do you replace them before they become dangerously worn?

Are mirrors placed away from fires/heaters, so you don't run the risk of standing too near?

Do you wash and bath safely, with a slip mat beside the bath, a rubber mat in the bath, and handles on the bath?

Safety in Medicines and Equipment:
Do you have a proper medicine cabinet?

Do you keep medicines in their original containers, clearly labelled?

Do you take medicines only at prescribed times and in correct doses?

Do you return left-over medicines to the chemist for disposal, rather than hoarding them at home?

Do you store medicine, bleach, weed-killer where grandchildren can't reach them?

Out of doors have you separate containers for hot ash and other rubbish (a lot of fires start if the two become mixed).

Safety Extras:
1. Grip rails by the bath and toilet.
2. A rubber mat, or plastic non-slip strips in the bath.
3. A handrail on the wall side of the stairs.
4. A smoke detector.
5. A fire extinguisher in the kitchen, and a fire blanket near at hand (in case of chip pan fire).
6. Flame resistant furnishing materials and paints.
7. A properly stocked medicine cabinet.
8. A first aid kit which should contain plasters, bandage, unmedicated sterile dressing, scissors, cotton wool, lint, antiseptic cream.
9. Send for *First Aid Index Chart*, published by the Health Education Bureau, an A-Z guide on what to do in any emergency from asthma to unconsciousness. Free from HEB, 34 Upper Mount Street, Dublin 2. Telephone: (01) 761116/766640.

Home Security: How can you make your home more burglar proof? 'You can't', says John Wainwright, author of *Guard Your Castle*, 'every lock, every bolt, every bar, the finest burglar alarm system in the world buys only one thing — time'. Ex-policeman Wainwright knows your would-be burglar well. 'We'll call him Bill Sykes. He knows his trade and can weigh the pros and the cons. He is not a house agent, he does not categorise property into detached, semi, bungalow, flat, maisonette or terrace type. He is a breaker. He uses a much simpler tabulatory system. Everything is either a Hard Number or a Soft Touch. Given time, he can break both types, but a quiet stroll into a Soft Touch is much preferable to risking a hernia by cracking a Hard Number.'

So how can you turn your Soft Touch into a Hard Number? Making your home a safer place to live in costs less than you may think. Beginning with the hall door, you can buy a five-lever mortice deadlock, which is sunk into the interior door rim. It offers anti-drill security cover, double-sided key operation, hardened steel deadbolt and solid steel box-type locking plate, a lock with one thousand key differentials, incapable of being picked, and immune to skeleton keys. A variety of these locks are available at locksmiths and hardware shops, average price under £50. They can be fitted by the DIY enthusiast.

Closing a Window is not Enough

A little plate on the house proclaims its presence. 'It will deter 90% of burglars', says a member of the Irish Security Industry Association, 'why should they take you on, when there's someone much easier down the street?' A similar mortice deadlock can also be fitted to the back and other exterior doors. But 60% of burglars enter our homes through a window, so merely closing it is not a deterrent. Made from sheet glass, it can be broken quite easily, without too much noise, leaving a hole wide enough to insert a hand to open the handle. A man can get in a 12" x 14" window. Once he can get his head in, and one arm, he can enter. There are many types of window

locks on the market today. One model locks the frame to the window, is operated with a key and costs under £10.

How about possessions at home? A 6" x 9" underfloor safe will cost about £200, including fitting and up to £500 will buy something large enough to hold the silver candlesticks, as well as cash, jewellery and small valuables. The safe will be difficult to locate, short of ripping up all the floorboards, and impossible to move if found, as it is set in mass concrete. A simple alarm system for the average home will cost from £500. This will give perimeter protection only, designed to discourage entry by sounding an alarm bell as the thief tries to enter by the door or window. Vengeful households may choose a silent alarm which rings only in the local police station, the theory being the thief will be caught as he is departing with your possessions. This type tends to be used more by commercial firms than private homes.

Security Firms

It is important to choose a reputable security firm, who will give effective advice, carry out the work properly, and still be around in six months time for the routine maintenance required. The Irish Security Industry Assocation was set up in 1972 to promote proper standards and now repre-sents over 75% of the security business here. Any association member dealing with private alarms, will visit households on request and advise on how to make homes more secure. There is no call out charge. The Crime Prevention Unit, Harcourt Square, Dublin 2, Telephone: (01) 732222, also has a list of reputable firms, and will furnish names to the public.

Every year about 30,000 homes are

burgled, with the value of stolen property running into millions of pounds. Then there is the emotional loss, the feeling of being violated, and our well-loved possessions taken or pawed over. Sometimes homes are left in a horrible condition. There is the fear of a repeat, the fear of coming back to an empty house, the reliving of the horror in our thoughts again and again. Prevention is always better than cure. The Crime Prevention people say that we are still far too trusting. 'The first principle', they say, 'is to keep the intruder out. Any little catch, screw, lock, anything that makes it more difficult for him to gain entry is good.' The unit has a small permanent exhibition, open to the public, allowing people to examine the different types of locks and bolts, and to get free advice on what is most suitable for each home. Exhibition is at Harcourt Square, Telephone: (01) 732222, (phone before you visit).

They also have a list of do's and don'ts:

Do lock all internal doors, this will slow the thief down if he does gain entry in your absence.

Don't lock small cabinets or pieces of furniture. It will arouse his interest, not deter him, and he will smash it to see what's inside.

Do inform your neighbours and ask them to be vigilant on your behalf, if you're away for the day or on holidays.

Don't leave small sums of money lying around as a sop. If people know money is available, they'll come more often and take it, and anything else as well.

Do inform the police station if you're away, they will note your address down in the holiday book, and patrol your road.

Don't swathe the place in dusty sheets, or draw the curtains, you might as well put an ad in the local paper announcing your absence.

Do cancel the milk by telephoning the dairy, not by leaving a note.

Don't forget to join your Neighbourhood Watch Scheme. The local police station will tell you if one has started in your area, and who to contact for help.

USEFUL CONTACTS AND REFERENCES

Crime Prevention Unit,
Harcourt Square,
Dublin 2.
Telephone: (01) 732222

Irish Security Industry Association,
463 Collins Avenue,
Dublin 9.
Telephone: (01) 374918

Technical Aids Information Section,
National Rehabilitation Board,
25 Clyde Road,
Dublin 4.
Telephone: (01) 684181

Exhibition of special home safety/mobility aids, apply for specific home aids through local Rehabilitation Board branches round the country:

6 Georges Quay, Cork. (021) 270423
58 Anne Street, Dundalk. (042) 32913
The Manse, Castle Street, Mullingar. (044) 40219
High Street, Tullamore. (0506) 41262
75 John Street, Waterford. (051) 74231
10 Ely Place, Sea Road, Galway. (081) 63567
Gt. Southern Grounds, Sligo. (071) 64267
Main Street, Castlebar. (094) 22169
Ballyraine Park, Letterkenny. (074) 21103
Glentworth Street, Limerick. (061) 31979
21 Pembroke Street, Tralee. (066) 23292
Bandon Street, Ennis. (065) 20141

Home from Home Report on boarding-out schemes for people in Ireland. Available from National Council of the Aged, Corrigan House, Fenian Street, Dublin 2.

The Fire Prevention Council,
32 Nassau Street,
Dublin 2.
Telephone: (01) 714070

Free advice on all aspects of fire prevention.

7. Looking After Your Health

Being healthy doesn't mean looking as thin as a whippet and running 16 miles a day. It's much wider than that. I met retired people, who never donned a tracksuit, and still have a healthy lifestyle. Seamus Fitzpatrick, a widower in his 70s, plays golf several times a week, watches what he eats, looks and feels well. James White, retired director of the National Gallery of Ireland continues the exercises he has done for years. 'I get out of bed in the morning and do bending and stretching exercises eight times, touch my toes eight times, come up into sitting position from lying down eight times, then get my feet up in the air and bicycle eight times'.

Leslie Mahon's exercise is confined to a few games of bowls each week, but he doesn't seem to have a tense bone in his body, and is enjoying retirement.

So being healthy means more than the size of your muscles. It includes mental and emotional as well as physical health. It has to do with how we look at life; our capacity for enjoyment and stimulation; how we relax; the condition of our body; our eating, drinking and smoking habits; how quickly we run out of puff when chasing a bus. But for many people, some form of physical exercise can be a key component to general good health. The reasons are that when we take some regular exercise, four good things happen:

> We get away from the four walls at home and become involved with other people.
>
> We begin to feel good about ourselves because we're putting effort in, and taking responsibility for our well-being.
>
> We get some immediate physical payback in more energy, suppleness and general 'oomph'.
>
> We may begin to be more aware of what we eat and drink, so there may be a spin-off affecting more good habits.

'I Lie Down Until it Passes Away'

Having said that, the general population seem to be fairly unfit. When asked what he did when he felt the urge to take exercise, Winston Churchill is said to have replied, 'I lie down until the feeling passes'. Many adults seem to follow his example. Despite the proliferation of joggers on our paths, and health clubs in our towns, surveys show that over 70% of the Irish population don't

60

take part in any organised sport at all. When we come to the 40-plus age group, the statistics become even poorer. Only two out of ten middle-aged people engage in any sporting activity. There are exceptions, of course, to every rule. Paddy Whelan from Walkinstown is in his mid-70s and runs 60 miles a week. Dick Rafferty, in his 70s, set up a world record in the high jump in his age group some years ago, and still trains regularly.

They are the exceptions. For many adults, the only regular exercise they get is bending the elbow to lower a pint. Why this national reluctance to get up and go? The reasons are both cultural and historical. For most boys, introduction to organised sport happened at school, and was accompanied by competition, coercion, and perhaps, ridicule at the unfit. So when boys became men, many abandoned sport with sighs of relief never to take it up again. Women in their 60s today had a different problem. Sport in girls' schools used to be more honoured in the breach than the observance. Up to comparatively recently, it was considered unladylike to sweat, and women got little encouragement to compete in sport.

Our Bodies are Under-Used

But in 50 years, our style of life has greatly changed in Ireland. A few generations ago, most people worked on the land, or in a job using physical energy. Today we have machines to do the hard, physical work for us at home, on the farm, in the factory. We travel by car, use lifts, push-buttons and other labour-saving gadgets, and our bodies become progressively under-used. The effect of this lack of exercise over years is dramatic. Simply put 'you either use it or lose it'. Joints which are not regularly put through a full range of movements become stiff, and the range of movements then become limited. Muscle strength declines rapidly with lack of use. Many middle-aged people have poor strength, particularly in the stomach and back regions, the muscles used for good posture, for walking and lifting.

Lack of vigorous exercise limits our stamina, our staying power, our ability to keep going without gasping for breath. This inhibits the blood circulation to the heart and lungs and makes for a sluggish system. Lack of exercise is linked by doctors to the spread of coronary heart disease today. All this inactivity has a cumulative effect. If you are unfit, you won't be able to walk very far, lift and carry very efficiently. You'll feel tired and lacking in energy. Mentally, you will feel less alert, you'll become inactive, and as a result, feel old. Many problems associated with being old are due to unfitness, not to disease and not to age.

So, the acid test, how unfit are you?

Are you left gasping for breath if you run a short distance, say 50 yards?

Does your heart thump after climbing a few flights of stairs?

Do you ache all over after digging a small patch of garden?

Are you tired out after an hour of strenuous housework?

Is it an effort to bend and tie your shoelaces?

Are you exhausted after carrying two bags of shopping for a quarter of a mile?

Are you jaded after mowing the lawn with a handmower?

Answer 'yes' to any of the above questions, and you can identify yourself as someone leading a fairly sedentary life, unused to much exercise.

So having looked at the ills that lack of exercise helps bring about, let's examine the subject positively and ask what exercise achieves. A person, irrespective of age, who is physically fit is supple, strong and has plenty of stamina. What does this mean?

Suppleness: The ability to bend, stretch, twist and turn as you wish. The more supple you are, the less likely to suffer from aches and pains caused by stiffness, to have accidents due to slow reaction.

Strength: Is extra muscle power needed for pushing, lifting, carrying. Strength is improved by regularly increasing the amount of effort required of your muscle.

Stamina: Is staying power, the ability to work harder for longer, to keep going without gasping for breath. This improves the circulation in the heart and lungs, because oxygen has to be pumped in sufficient quantities to the working muscles. The more vigorous the exercise, the greater the demand for oxygen in the blood, and the better the exercise for heart and lungs.

So the best reason for getting fit is that you'll feel so good as a result. But before launching into a vigorous programme, have a look at your current lifestyle. Many of your everyday activities already provide good opportunities for exercise: a brisk walk, climbing stairs, gardening, and housework such as washing clothes by hand, scrubbing and polishing.

Have a look at your daily routine, and see if you can find other ways of becoming more active. A few tips to begin with:

> Abandon the lift and begin walking upstairs.
>
> Leave the car in the garage a few times a week and walk to and from local shops.
>
> Buy a dog, it will get you out.

And if you do decide on something more vigorous, here are four more golden rules to follow before you begin:

> Ask your doctor to give you the go-ahead.
>
> Start each exercise at the lowest level.
>
> Progress slowly and gently, if it hurts, it's wrong.
>
> Don't become too competitive until you've built up a good level of suppleness, strength and stamina.

How and Where to Begin?

You could do worse than see if there is a Saol Plus organisation in your area. Saol Plus is a movement specially geared to bring the joys of exercise to the great unjogged. Their sessions are for people who may not have worked-out for years, and come for enjoyment and participation, rather than white heat competitiveness. The Saol Plus sessions at your local club will include warm up sessions, isometrics (relaxation and contraction of muscles), dance, movement to music, trampoline, volleyball, tunnelball, relay and other games. And the Saol Plus philosophy also encompasses sailing, orienteering, table tennis and more, anything to get older people up and doing.

'The aim', says Jerry Kelly, well-known for his routines on RTE's *Good Afternoon* programme: 'is enjoyment-quality exercise.

Many older people underestimate what they can do, and only need a bit of encouragement to make a start'. He is one of the prime movers in Saol Plus. Health clubs all over the country are now setting up sessions, and for a national register, contact Saol Plus, Loughlinstown Leisure Centre, Co. Dublin. Telephone: (01) 823344.

Meanwhile Jerry has devised the following exercise programme for unfit middle-aged to elderly readers wanting to get into shape. He includes a variety of supported and free positions, different degrees of force, body shape and directional change. The exercises may be done to music (he suggests you use them to make up your own routine), alone at home, or with a partner, or out with a group. Before beginning, Jerry too counsels caution. 'If you have not exercised for some time, start slowly. Consult your doctor before you start. Encourage some of your friends to take part with you, wear loose comfortable clothing, try to exercise in a warm, pleasant environment, only exercising when you feel like it, do as much as you can, and don't overdo it'.

Programme:

Sitting in Chair:
(repeat five to ten times)
1. Head — turn left, right, hold - alternate.
2. Shoulders — hunch, rotate - alternate.
3. Arms — lift overhead and back to side.
4. Hands — clasp together and lift overhead.
5. Hands — hold in front, move left/right.
6. Arms — crawl, breast stroke.
7. Hands — shake in front, overhead.

8. Fingers — thumb to index/middle/ring/little.
9. Arms — over side of chair and reach down to side - alternate.
10. Back — feet flat on floor, lean forward, hands clasped between knees.
11. Feet — stamp feet.
12. Legs — swing leg back/forward/circle.
13. Feet — toes on floor, back on to heels.

Standing:
(repeat five to ten times)

1. Feet apart, swing arms round in circles.
2. Pull chain with arms.
3. Drop alternate shoulders from side to side.
4. Bend to touch alternate toes.
5. Stand up on toes, back on heels.
6. Up on toes, bend legs, straighten up.

On Floor:
(repeat five to ten times)

1. On back bend legs, lift bottom.
2. Lift left leg and right arm straight, alternate.
3. Tighten toes toward chest, legs straight.
4. Resting on arms, cycle action with legs, one leg at a time.
5. Rest on arms, bend leg, rotate toes.

Standing with Scarf:
(repeat five to ten times)

1. Holding scarf in front, roll into ball with hands.
2. Holding scarf in front, roll up.
3. Scarf behind back, stretch from side to side.
4. Holding scarf out in front, select music and move to rythem with - scarf in front, to the side, overhead, down to toes, behind back.

Standing with sponge ball:
(hold for count of ten)

1. Out in front, squeeze.
2. Overhead, squeeze.
3. Down at toes, squeeze.

4. To side, squeeze.
5. Behind back, squeeze.
6. On head, squeeze.
7. On floor, between legs, squeeze.
8. *On back*, bend knees, ball between knees, squeeze.

Using sponge ball and partner:

1. Passing ball back and forth.
2. Stand back to back, pass ball from side to side.
3. Pass ball over head and back under legs.

Exercise with Partner - Standing:
(repeat five to ten times)

1. Face partner, hold hands and alternate bending forward.
2. Stand behind, lift partner's arms.
3. On one leg, lift leg to side, (partner support).
4. On one leg, rotate toes, (partner support).
5. Kneel opposite partner, hold hands and begin rowing action.

Movement to Music:
Select march tune and with music:

1. Low knee lift.
2. High knee lift.
3. Introduce arms.
4. Turn from side to side.
5. Round in circles.
6. Formation.

Select tune with steady beat:

1. Swing arms from side to side.
2. Swing out hands.
3. Twist arms side to side.
4. Three steps forwards, backwards and clap.
5. Rotate feet.
6. Move three paces left, right and clap.
7. Turn in circles.
8. Move forwards and backwards bending and reaching.

(Note: this routine will also be found in *Get Fit, Stay Fit* Dolmen Press, by Jerry Kelly, published November, 1985).

What other kinds of exercise do you good? The following health chart was devised by the Health Education Bureau, and it scores activities on the criteria of suppleness, strength and stamina:

	suppleness	strength	stamina
swimming	***	***	***
cycling	*	**	***
running	*	**	***
keep fit classes	**	**	***
disco dancing	**	**	***
squash	***	**	**
football	**	**	**
housework	**	**	*
climbing stairs	*	**	**
walking briskly	*	*	**
badminton/tennis	**	**	**

Swimming scores best under all headings, and the increase in indoor heated pools means that many older people are swimming regularly. I met one 69-year-old who took it up a few years ago, and now swims with fellow members of her active retirement association every week. She also plays bowls and is a member of a walking group. She also says she has slowed up a bit in the past ten years, but still enjoys all her physical activities and knows they're keeping her feeling young.

Being healthy also means knowing how to relax. Total relaxation of the body is an effective way of dealing with stress. It helps to calm the mind, so that we are better able to cope with problems. Before we can relax, we must learn to recognise muscle tension. When we are under strain, we often hold our muscles tense, without realising it. It is possible to control this tension, by learning to relax the muscles which tighten up; once people learn the difference between a tense and a relaxed muscle, they can relax whenever they feel the need.

How to Relax: Find a quiet room, sit comfortably or lie down. Start by taking two or three deep breaths, breathe in slowly and fill lungs completely. See that tummy rises first, then chest, hold breath for just a few seconds, then breathe out slowly. This exercise relaxes and calms the breathing.

To relax the rest of the body, start at the toes, and tell each part to relax until reaching the top of the head. Just let go deliberately, bit by bit, toes, ankles, legs, tummy, up through the chest, arms, back, shoulders, neck. . . let everything go heavy and dead. At this stage, you will feel the chair, bed or floor pressing on the body because it will be a dead weight. Stay like that for about ten minutes, thinking positive thoughts if possible, then get up slowly and stretch the whole body gently. A daily relaxation session like this will help lessen the effects of stress in your life. It is also useful to talk about what is causing any stress — this may help stop the strain building up.

Ten other things to do to stop your emotions taking over:

Talk it over.

Escape for a while.

Work off your anger.

Give in occasionally.

Do something for someone else.

Take one thing at a time.

Don't be a perfectionist.

Give the other guy a chance.

Make yourself available to others.

Take some exercise.

Overweight

If you are overweight, you won't be as healthy as you could be. First, you will find it hard to exercise to improve that strength, suppleness and stamina. Internally, your joints are probably being asked to bear more weight than they should, so it's putting a strain on them. Also your heart has a difficult job pushing blood around a fatty body. You'll feel depressed about yourself. You won't look as nice as you could. You may feel guilty, despise yourself for being a glutton, clothes won't fit well, and you may begin staying in rather than going out.

How can you break this vicious circle? The best way to lose weight is to eat differently. Using the widely accepted traffic light system, divide foods into green, orange and red, representing the go ahead, then proceed with caution, and the absolutely stop food groups.

Green light foods include all fresh fruits except avocados: lettuce, tomatoes, green and root vegetables, white fish, poultry, cottage cheese, skimmed milk, clear soups, low calorie soft drinks, artificial sweetener, tea, coffee, water.
Eat these foods most.

Orange light foods are meat, eggs, milk, oily fish, cheese, beans, yogurt, bread, cereals, pasta, potatoes, rice. Use butter/margarine for bread only.
Limit your intake of these foods.

Red light foods are sugars, sweets, cakes, ice cream, chocolate (including the diabetic variety), pastry, biscuits, desserts, jam, honey, marmalade, tinned fruit, cream, salad dressing, chips, thick soups, sauces, cooking fats/oils, all fried foods, sausages, pies, white pudding, stuffing, fat on meat, skin on poultry, soft drinks, all alcoholic drinks.
Avoid these foods while trying to lose weight. When you arrive at your target weight — continue to see them as treats to be taken occasionally.

A Balanced Diet

The food we eat, or don't eat, has a big effect on how healthy or not we are. Eating the wrong food is an underlying cause of many diseases, particularly in the 50-plus age group, and a balanced diet is the foundation for good health at every age. By a balanced diet we mean one that gives us all the different nutrients we need in the correct amount. Each nutrient has a particular job to do in our body, and a deficiency can lead to a specific ailment. These days dieticians make the job of choosing a balanced diet relatively easy by dividing food into four groups, explaining what nutrients are provided by each group, and the jobs they do.

The four groups are:
1. *The milk group:* which includes milk, cheese, yogurt and skimmed or low fat milk.

This group provides protein which is used to build and repair body tissue, bone, muscle and skin. It has calcium for healthy bone development, teeth, and muscle function. It contains fat, a concentrated source of energy. Vitamin A helps towards healthy eyes and skin. Vitamin B enables the body to use the energy in food, and is necessary for the prevention of anaemia, and for the maintenance of a healthy nervous system. Vitamin D helps the body to absorb and use calcium.

2. *The meat group:* which includes meat of all kinds, poultry, fish, eggs, cheese, nuts and the pulse vegetables — peas, beans and lentils.

This group also provides protein, fat and Vitamin B but also iron which is important in the formation of red blood cells and in the prevention of anaemia.

3. *The fruit and vegetable group:* contains all fruits and vegetables, cooked or raw.

This group contains carbohydrates, a source of energy, and fibre, which is necessary for a healthy digestive system. It provides vitamins including Vitamin A for healthy eyes and skin, and Vitamin C which helps with healthy skin and gums, with wound-healing, and enabling the body to absorb iron.

4. *The bread and cereals group:* consists of bread, flour, biscuits, pasta, breakfast cereals, porridge, potatoes, rice.

This group also has carbohydrates for energy. It contains fibre (particularly present in wholewheat pasta, bread, flour and cereal), and it also provides protein and Vitamin B.

You will ensure a balanced diet by including foods from each group every day. It is important to have either milk, meat, poultry, fish, eggs, or cheese every day. Once a week eat organ meat (liver, heart or kidney), and oily fish like sardines, herring, mackerel or tuna. Dietician Catherine McCarthy would like to see people have a good breakfast with fruit or fruit juice, cereal, tea/coffee, bread, preferably wholemeal bread every day. Skimping on breakfast, she says, is a bad policy, because it leads to sugary elevenses to assuage mid-morning hunger pangs. A leisurely breakfast is one of the perks of retirement, and after a lifetime of dashing off after a hasty cuppa, it should be enjoyed.

She makes an important general point about food. 'Meals are more than food. They are a social occasion, so try and make them as pleasant as possible. There is a term called widower's scurvy, which affects men unable to cook, living on tea and boiled eggs, too narrow and too poor a diet. Women can neglect themselves too — after been used to cooking for a large family, when left on their own they won't take the trouble, and could end up with poor,

unappetising meals'. Catherine suggests that people who live alone should try and turn a meal into an occasion by inviting a friend to eat with them regularly. 'Take fruit or fruit juice at least once a day', she says, 'plus at least one vegetable, raw or cooked every day, and a minimum of two slices of wholemeal bread, (even if you're trying to lose weight).

'Make sure you get a good amount of fibre by eating wholemeal bread, wholegrain breakfast cereal, and plenty of fruit and vegetables, including potatoes. Fibre will help prevent constipation, and other disorders of the digestive system.' Foods particularly good for older people are liver, with its valuable iron, which prevents anaemia; (it doesn't have to be a hard dry piece, casserole it, or bake it with bacon and stuffing), also oily fish, including tinned fish, the best source of Vitamin D, which helps prevent the onset of brittle bones so common in elderly people. 'Don't put bread soda in the cabbage,' she warns 'it destroys the Vitamin C. Preferably go for low-fat milk, and use three-quarters to one pint a day to ensure an adequate calcium intake.'

'As people grow older, their metabolism slows down gradually, so they do not need to eat as much. If they continue to eat the same amount, and don't work it off, it will be stored on the body in great layers of fat. So while you need less food as you get older, this means less in terms of quantity only. The body's need for all the nutrients is the same as in younger adulthood, and in the case of one or two nutrients, may even be increased. Also in later life, the digestive tract may not be quite as efficient at absorbing the nutrients from food, so it is especially important that foods eaten are of high nutritional value'.

Store Cupboards

So people should try and avoid sugar, which Catherine says is full of 'empty calories', and devoid of protein, vitamins and minerals. Also foods high in sugar tend to contain a lot of fat, for example, cakes and biscuits. She suggests people also ease up on tinned foods, because many of these have a high salt content. Salt can raise blood pressure in susceptible individuals, and could be harmful in large quantities. A store cupboard is important for people who can't get out in cold or icy weather. 'It shouldn't', says Catherine, 'mean a dozen packs of soup and a square of jelly. A properly planned store cupboard should be able to provide a balanced diet for several days, and contain foods from the four main groups'.

A store cupboard should contain:

Skimmed milk powder or tinned evaporated milk.

Small tins of meat and fish.

Dried and tinned vegetables.

Tinned fruit (packed in fruity juice not sugary syrup).

Fruit juice, bottled, tinned or dried; choose one labelled 'with Vitamin C'.

Instant mashed potato mix, with Vitamin C.

Crackers, digestive biscuits and crispbread.

Oatmeal and breakfast cereal.

Ingredients for milk pudding, e.g. rice, semolina, custard powder.

Cocoa, Ovaltine, Horlicks, Complan.

Soup and sauce mixes.

Marmite, Bovril.

Drugs and Medicines

Cigarettes: Many people in the 40-plus age group began smoking as youngsters before the harmful effects of smoking were realised. Today the weight of evidence against cigarette smoking is enormous. It can shorten life, damage lungs, chest and heart and lead to cancer of the throat and lungs. What smokers may still not realise is that these damaging effects can be offset from the day they stop smoking, and the organs begin to return to their former splendour. So it's worth stopping, whether you've smoked for ten, 20, even 30 years. You'll feel a lot better, your food will taste much nicer, and you will be giving good example to children and grandchildren.

How to stop? Decide you're going to, give yourself about three weeks to get from present level to zero. Get literature on the subject from the Irish Heart Foundation, the Irish Cancer Society or the Health Promotion Unit at the Department of Health to strengthen your resolve to be rid of the filthy weed forever. Tell family and friends you intend giving up cigarettes, so that they won't offer you any, and will put up with your grouchiness. Try and begin the new campaign with friend or spouse. Begin on a day like National No-Smoking Day (Spring each year), and get the support of the nation.

Change your habits for a while; don't frequent places where you know you will smoke, and vary your lifestyle by doing something new to break the habits that bind you to smoking. Think of all the money you're saving and put it aside for a holiday, or something you've always wanted. Try and avoid the temptation to substitute sweets for cigarettes.

Alcohol: This is our social drug of greatest use and abuse. In moderation it is pleasant,

68

lifts the spirit, muzzles inhibitions, makes us all sparkle in company, and gives conversation that extra zip. But the chemical is highly addictive; abuse can harm the body physically, change personalities, and can lead to a physical dependency and a mental attitude to reach for a drink instead of facing up to a problem. Nationally, alcohol contributes significantly to road traffic accidents and fatalities, to absenteeism from work on a grand scale, to family violence, poverty and hardship, to physical and psychological illness.

If you feel you are beginning to drink too much too often, you can stop in time. The awareness is the first step. Have a look at the underlying problems which may be leading to the abuse in the first place. Realise what is happening to you, you're becoming addicted. Talk it over with someone. Try and substitute something else for the hours you spend drinking. If you can't stop on your own, get help. Your local GP will have information on local agencies. Hereunder is a list of national addresses:

Organisations where people with alcohol-related problems may get advice or treatment:

The Irish National Council
  on Alcoholism,
(INCA) 19/20 Fleet Street,
Dublin 2.
Telephone: (01) 774832

Alcoholics Anonymous, (AA),
109 South Circular Road,
Dublin 8.
Telephone: (01) 538998

Al-Anon Family Groups and
  Al-Ateen Information Centre,
12 Westmoreland Street,
Dublin 2. ·
Telephone: (01) 774195

Alcoholism Counselling Centre,
24 Dame Street,
Dublin 2.
Telephone: (01) 716323

Alcoholism Counselling Centre,
65 Lucan Road,
Chapelizod, Co. Dublin.
Telephone: (01) 267572

The Hanly Centre,
The Mews, Eblana Avenue,
Dun Laoire,
Co. Dublin.
Telephone: (01) 809795

Stanhope Alcoholic Counselling Service,
Stanhope Street,
Dublin 2.
Telephone: (01) 779447

Rutland Treatment Centre,
Knocklyon House,
Dublin 16.
Telephone: (01) 773965

Alcoholics Rehabilitation Centre,
Cuan Mhuire,
Cardington, Athy,
Co. Kildare.
Telephone: (0507) 31564

Aiseiri Treatment Centre,
Cahir,
Co. Tipperary.
Telephone: (052) 41192

Drugs & Alcohol Treatment Centre,
Arbour House,
St Finbar's Hospital,
Cork.
Telephone: (021) 968933

Treatment Facilities in Health Board Areas:

Eastern

Public:
St Brendan's,
Upper Grangegorman,
Dublin 7.
Telephone: (01) 302844

St Dymphna's,
North Circular Road,
Dublin 7.
Telephone: (01) 302844

St Ita's,
Portrane,
Co. Dublin.
Telephone: (01) 450337

St Loman's,
Palmerstown,
Co. Dublin.
Telephone: (01) 264077

Newcastle Hospital,
Co. Wicklow.
Telephone: (01) 819233

Jervis Street Hospital,
Dublin 1.
Telephone: (01) 748412

Private:

St John of God Hospital,
Stillorgan,
Co. Dublin.
Telephone: (01) 881781

St Patrick's Hospital,
James's Street,
Dublin 8.
Telephone: (01) 775423

Edmondsbury,
Lucan,
Co. Dublin.
Telephone: (01) 280211

South Eastern

Public:
St Dymphna's Hospital,
Carlow.
Telephone: (0503) 31106

St Luke's,
Clonmel,
Co. Tipperary.
Telephone: (052) 22300

St Canice's,
Kilkenny.
Telephone: (056) 21341

St Otteran's,
Waterford.
Telephone: (051) 74991

St Joseph's,
Clonmel,
Co. Tipperary.
Telephone: (057) 21900

Private:
St Patrick's,
Belmont Park,

Waterford.
Telephone: (051) 32211

Bon Sauveur Home,
Carrigla, Dungargan,
Co. Waterford.
Telephone: (058) 41322

North Eastern

Public:
St Brigid's Hospital,
Ardee,
Co. Louth.
Telehone: (041) 53264

St Davnet's,
Monaghan.
Telephone: (047) 81822

Southern

Public:
Our Lady's Hospital,
Cork.
Telephone: (021) 41901

St Raphael's Hospital,
Youghal,
Co. Cork.
Telephone: (024) 2422

St Finan's,
Killarney,
Co. Kerry.
Telephone: (064) 31022

St Stephen's,
Sarsfield Court,
Cork.
Telephone: (021) 508222

St Anne's,
Skibbereen,
Co. Cork.
Telephone: (028) 21677

Private:
Lindville,
Blackrock Road,
Cork.
Telephone: (021) 292482

Mid-Western

Public:
Our Lady's Hospital,
Ennis,
Co. Clare.
Telephone: (065) 21414

St Joseph's,
Limerick.
Telephone; (061) 46166

Western
Public:
St Brigid's Hospital,
Ballinasloe,
Co. Galway.
Telephone: (0905) 42117
St Patrick's,
Castlerea,
Co. Roscommon.
Telephone: (0907) 20016
St Mary's,
Castlebar,
Co. Mayo.
Telephone: (094) 21333

North Eastern
Public:
St Conal's,
Letterkenny,
Co. Donegal.
Telephone: (074) 21022
St Columba's,
Sligo.
Telephone: (071) 2111

Midland
Public:
St Loman's,
Mullingar,
Co. Westmeath.
Telephone: (044) 80191
St Fintan's,
Portlaoise,
Co. Laois.
Telephone: (0502) 21103

In addition to all these places, people with problems relating to alcohol can get help in the psychiatric units attached to some general hospitals, and also in some private nursing homes.

Legally Prescribed Drugs: There is a place in medicine for drugs that heal, inhibit and treat infection. But not all drugs are good for us. People regularly go to their doctor with problems, looking for something to help them cope. Some doctors, unable to help with life situations, succumb to pressure from patients and write a prescription for tranquillisers or anti-depressants to help them manage. As a nation we consume twelve million pounds worth of tranquillisers each year. Some of these are highly addictive, people could become dependent in a matter of weeks, and some experience severe withdrawal problems if they try to stop taking the drug. Also, we can build up a tolerance fairly quickly, so the beneficial effect, if any, wears away. Drugs are not the answer for many of life's problems. Facing up to the problem will usually be much more constructive, getting help, talking it over with a friend, making our decision. Remember the relaxation and coping techniques already discussed.

Body Finite

As we have said, there are many diseases associated with ageing that have nothing to do with growing old. But we can't hold back the hand of time completely. Bits of our bodies do begin to wear out as we grow older. This is what we should be aware of:

Eyes: As we get older the lenses of the eye tend to become less flexible, and our eyes lose some of their focussing power. This means that most people over 45 have to hold a book or newspaper further away to focus on the print correctly. Many have to think of glasses for the first time. Get the eyes tested every few years, report to the doctor any of the following symptoms: coloured haloes around eyes, seeing better in twilight than in daylight, being easily dazzled.

Ears: Most people experience hearing loss as they get older, which is caused by changes in the inner mechanism of the ear. As soon as you realise you're having to ask people to repeat themselves often, go to the doctor. It might be just wax which when cleaned will give dramatically improved effects. If you need a hearing aid, get proper advice on types from the Hearing Aid Centre, National Rehabilitation Board, 25 Clyde Road, Dublin 4. Telephone: (01) 689618.

Joints: Arthritis is the wearing out of joints, and occurs typically at knee, hip and vertebrae, causing stiffness and pain, sometimes very severe. The thing to remember is that arthritis is a disease, not a penalty of being old. It can be treated. Go to the doctor, who will be able to offer medication; joint replacement operations are now performed very successfully, giving many people a new lease of life.

Teeth: By the age of 50, two out of five have lost their own teeth and wear dentures. Much of this loss would have been prevented by more correct and frequent brushing, a less sugary diet, and regular dental check-ups. But even in the best regulated mouths, teeth may be lost through shrinking, receding gums. Get into the habit of six monthly check-ups with the dentist.

USEFUL CONTACTS AND REFERENCES

The Voluntary Health Insurance Board,
VHI House,
20 Lower Abbey Street,
Dublin 1.
Telephone: (01) 724499

The VHI was founded to provide protection to people against the cost of serious illness. It provides cover for maintenance and treatment in hospitals and nursing homes. Out-patient benefits are also available. The upper age limit for joining is 65 and special entry conditions usually apply to applicants over 55.

Health Promotion Unit
Department of Health,
Hawkins House,
Hawkins Street,
Dublin 2.
Publishes *Back Care, Better Health Guide, Put Your Heart Into It*, all free.

Saol Plus,
Loughlinstown Leisure Centre,
Co. Dublin.
Telephone; (01) 823344

Irish Heart Foundation,
4 Clyde Road,
Dublin 4.
Telephone: (01) 685010

Irish Cancer Society,
5 Northumberland Road,
Dublin 4.
Telephone: (01) 681855

Tranx Release,
31 Mount Pleasant Square,
Ranelagh,
Dublin 6.

For people wanting to come off tranquillisers. They hold meetings every Tuesday 8.30 p.m.

Shop 'n Save Book
A guide to good eating on a budget, free from:
The National Savings Committee,
21 Earlsfort Terrace,
Dublin 2.
Telephone: (01) 766305

Arthritis Foundation of Ireland,
1 Sydney Parade Avenue,
Dublin 4.
Telephone: (01) 691737

Publishes free books and leaflets to help people
cope with arthritis and rheumatism.

National Road Safety Association,
4 Northbrook Road,
Dublin 6.
Telephone: (01) 963422

Operates a reflective armband scheme for
people over 60. It is available through health
centres and local authorities from the Road
Safety Officer.

8. Coping With Loss

When June O'Riordan's husband died seven years ago she had a nervous break-down. A mother of five, they had both been involved parents and even though the family was grown up, after his death, she felt frightened, indecisive, alone. She felt guilty about the rows and difficulties they had had, and used go over these in her mind, some-times becoming very upset. She made a few mistakes. She moved soon after the death, sold off much of her furniture, and moved to be near a daughter in an area where she had few contacts.

After a spell in hospital, June was helped by a psychotherapist, who showed her how to face up to her fears, both real and stress-induced. She slowly and laboriously worked through her grief. She says it takes about three years and much courage to cope with widowhood. She still misses her husband, prays to him, and talks to him in many of her difficulties. She has found new interests, joined a choir, and renewed her interest in the women's club, that she had let lapse during his illness. Living alone now, she copes quite well. She sees her family often. She enjoys crosswords, reading, radio, television, sewing, gardening and walking, and keeps body and mind as active as possible.

We All Helped Each Other

Seamus Fitzpatrick's wife, Nell, died of cancer over 20 years ago, leaving him eight children to rear, aged 19 to five. He hadn't much time for grieving, and had to get on with the business of rearing. How did he cope? 'One of the helpful things was that I never had any guilt. I did everything in my earthly power for her, she was wonderful, I could never have accepted death as she did. I was very busy with the children. We helped one another. I consul-ted them about everything; budgeting, decorating, cooking — the girls were my great helpers'. Seamus at 71 now lives on his own. The family are reared and many live nearby. His mantelpiece is festooned with photos of grandchildren, he is a very involved grandad, babysits often, and even bakes regularly for his daughters.

He has carved out a busy lifestyle for himself. As chairperson of his local active retirement association, he puts in an appearance at the centre every morning, to meet members and deal with any queries. He plays golf every weekend, makes his own wine, and is a member of a musical society. He reads a lot (Roget's *Thesauras* stands open on the table, he loves words). He is very fit, gave up cigarettes in his 60s, dances most younger people off their feet, and stands on his head for his grandchildren.

Seamus has always been a good cook. He believes in a proper well-cooked meal every evening, with the table carefully set, the fire blazing nicely, and a glass of wine. He has adapted well to life on his own. Single people who spend many years looking after their parents have particular problems when they die. One such woman felt bewildered and had to come to terms with loss of role. 'I couldn't settle down to anything for ages. I was so used to rushing home from work to get her meal. The house seemed very empty, and I suddenly had all this time to myself that I didn't know what to do with.'

Coping Alone

We have 175,000 widows and widowers aged 45 and over in this country, and many have great difficulty coming to terms with their loss. We have thousands of single men and women, many of them devoted sons and daughters who spend many years looking after an elderly parent. Bereavement counsellor Delma O'Regan explains how someone feels when a close relative dies. 'People go through a phase of numbness, shock, not believing it has happened. There can be a great sense of unreality, which can carry on into denial where people continue to act as if it hasn't happened. Then there may be a mixture of anger and sadness, anger at why did this happen, why didn't the ambulance come sooner, why didn't the doctor refer earlier? Anger at the person that died, for dying. This anger may turn inwards into guilt.

'There can be a loss of self-identity. In a close relationship, you see yourself in the other person, when she or he goes, part of your own view of yourself is gone'. Over and above all else, there can be a great sense of loss, characterised by depression, help-lessness, feelings of anxiety, tension. 'A person at this stage is in a dependent situation', says Delma, 'open to suggestions, very vulnerable. There is no ability to make connection with the world, all energies are tied up in an inward struggle'. There can also be physical symptoms. The most common are lumps in the throat and stomach, difficulty in swallowing, tightness in the chest, and the need for frequent sighs. There is a high mortality rate among grieving spouses, more frequent visits to the doctor, and psychiatric referral in the time following a death.

Grieving

How can people help themselves? 'Uncork the bottle', says Delma simply, 'allow yourself to grieve. Find someone with whom you feel safe and talk and listen, and let yourself cry. A lot of the physical symptoms like lumps in the throat, chest and abdominal tension are the consequence of unshed tears. Let them out. Realise that the mixture you feel of anger and loss is normal. You are not going mad. I encourage people to project their anger, it may often be justified. Don't avoid going to the funeral, it will help you face up to the reality of the loss, and create something real for you to grieve about. For this reason, I believe death and its immediate aftermath should be handled without drug therapy, if possible. Drugs block reality, and don't help people face up to what is happening. Later, if there is insomnia, something may be needed for a while.'

'Thirdly, don't make major decisions too soon after a death. Some people move house to escape from memories at a time when they're in no fit state to make the decisions. Wait'. What of the role of family, friends and neighbours? 'Ideally a bereavement should be a time of openness,' says Delma, 'and the positive side of a death can be the breaking down of barriers within families, as people grow closer through shared pain.'

Often, however, pain isolates. A widow may be discouraged from talking about her husband, a daughter about a parent, as listeners become embarrassed by her tears. 'This happens because many adults have a lot of undissolved material inside themselves', says Delma, 'they are afraid that if they allow someone to talk about a bereavement, their own floodgates will open, and they can't cope with this. Also, we must make allowances in families. People handle grief in different ways. A woman will often say her son or daughter appeared cold and uncaring, but they are probably dealing with their father's death in their own way.'

When Does The Grieving Stop?

When does the grieving stop? 'Many people work their way through to an initial acceptance by 13 months', says Delma, 'or after the first anniversary. But there is no absolute rule, and some say the second year is the hardest when they face up to the reality of the loss. A person needs permission to stop grieving, and it is normal to get on with life again. People often say to me, "but I don't want to forget, I want to grieve". My response is you want to be able to remember wholly, remember the joy and the good times to, so you're allowed remember happily in the end.'

Very many people are helped through loss by their own spiritual beliefs. 'We were able to speak openly before she died,' says Dermot Meehan, a widower with three growing children, 'and we comforted each other by the thought, which we both sincerely believe that we will be united again in Heaven. I miss her dreadfully, and yet I can feel her presence. If I didn't believe in an after-life, if I felt this is all there is, all the suffering would have no meaning or purpose, and I would find life very hard to bear'. Many people I spoke to echoed Dermot's thoughts, and spoke of God as a familiar friend to whom they turn in good and bad times.

Journalist Hilary Boyle, who has managed on her own for many years, with limited resources offers the following human antidotes to loneliness.

> Use free travel to get back in touch with old friends.
>
> Talk to people at bus stops.
>
> Go for walks, talk to gardeners and young mothers with babies.
>
> Read, use your local library to study, and find a new interest.
>
> Visit someone worse off than you.

Practical Steps

Are there practical steps people can take to minimise the difficulties which occur when someone dies? Lots, according to the National Association of Widows in Ireland. They say that seven out of ten brides will end up as widows, but it's a prospect most women don't like to face, so they pretend it will never happen, and are bereft practically as well as emotionally when it does. 'Some men shield their wives from all financial matters,' says Eileen Procter, founder member of the widow's association, 'and very many women are content to leave matters that way. They don't know the first thing about bank accounts, mortgage repayments or finance. Often they are so shocked when their husband dies, they are not in a fit condition to make decisions, and can be pressurised into making quite the wrong ones'.

So how can a wife make practical provision? If she doesn't know already, she should begin to find out how much it costs to run the home, what's going out in insurances, mortgage repayments or rent, bills, income tax and the rest: 'You would be surprised at the number of women who don't know how to open a bank account, and have never written a cheque in their lives', says Hilary Shannon, development manager with the Retirement Planning Council, 'often the only money they've had control of is the housekeeping every week'. Men often keep their wives in ignorance of financial matters, but the conspiracy of silence may be thoughtless rather than malicious.

Making a Will

Many men don't want to think about their mortality either. Just over half those reaching retirement I met, had made a will — the others had been meaning to get around to it, but not yet. If a man dies without leaving a will, his assets become frozen and his family have no access to his money. This is awful at a time when they need immediate cash to pay both undertaker and milk bill, and will be ill-equipped to deal with financial hassle.

When there is no will, the estate will be distributed according to the Succession Act of 1965, with the whole going to the wife if there are no children or if there are, two-thirds to her, and eventually one-third to the children. The absence of a will creates delays. There will be no executor to carry out the wishes of the dead person. An administrator, usually the wife has to be appointed, and she has to apply for a grant of administration before any action can be taken. The whole thing can take months and costs more. If there is a will, the man's wishes are known, and can be put into effect usually more speedily.

Most men make a simple will leaving everything to their wives, and the bank can release a sum to carry her over while affairs are being sorted out. A solicitor gives three good reasons why people should make a will. 'First by making a will, you ensure that your property passes to the people of your choice. Secondly, you may choose the person whom you wish to look after your affairs on your death, this person is called the executor. Thirdly, you may mitigate the amount of inheritance tax payable by taking legal advice when you make your will. Even though you do make a will, this does not mean you give up any rights to your assets while alive. A will only takes effect at your death, nobody gets anything until your death, and you may at any time change your will during your life.'

Consult a Solicitor

'If you do not make a will, your spouse will get two-thirds of your estate, and the remaining one-third will go equally between your children. At first glance this may seem a fair way of disposing of one's assets. But is it? You may have an incapacitated child for whom you wish to set up a trust. Perhaps you would like to leave something to a charity, or to an old friend. The remoter the degree of relationship between the deceased and the beneficiary, the more likelihood of unfairness. When you have made up your mind to make a will, make a list of assets, including such things as insurance policies. List your creditors also, as they will have first call on your assets at death. Next, decide on whom you want to benefit under your will, and decide who is to be an executor'.

When making a will, people should consult a solicitor, rather than picking up a DIY form at the local newsagent. A survey of the numbers of invalid wills each year shows that a high proportion are the Do-It-Yourself variety. A beneficiary cannot be a witness, and if a spouse witnesses a will of which she or he is a beneficiary, as sometimes happens, the bequest to the wit-

78

nessing spouse does not take effect, and she or he may get nothing. Solicitors also help with phraseology. 'People say things like 'I leave the farm to Jack, and I trust he'll look after Mary', this won't do at all. A solicitor is an expert in phraseology, and he will know how best to set out your wishes in precise and legal language. People know in general what they want to do, but don't always know how to put it into words to make it happen.

Joint Bank Accounts

Financial matters flow much more smoothly when the couple have a joint bank account. If one spouse dies, the account continues automatically in the name of the survivor. Similarly with the family home. If the home is held in joint names as joint tenants, it automatically becomes the survivor's sole property on the spouse's death. Having the home changed from single to joint ownership is now a simple matter. Fees are controlled by the Family Home Protection Act, no stamp duty or registration fee is payable, and the legal costs are modest.

Finally, many women would probably be able to administer their late husband's affairs more easily if they could find all the documentation. But many men squirrel away a mass of papers unknown to their wives — the will itself, insurance policies, investment certificates, house deeds, and, most significantly, bank account details. Finding the money after a husband dies is often a big problem. All this would be avoided if people were persuaded to keep a check-list of documentation, with the papers, particularly the will, in a safe, secure place.

The Institute of Chartered Accountants in Ireland has produced a check-list called *Where my Possessions are Kept*. It lists everything from family heirlooms to stocks to credit cards. The completion of this eight page yellow folder by a caring spouse, could literally be a lifeline to his remaining partner. Coping with the loss of a loved one is difficult enough, but it can be made unbearable by unnecessary financial ignorance.

USEFUL CONTACTS AND REFERENCES

Samaritans,
112 Marlborough Street,
Dublin 1.
Telephone: (01) 727700

Samaritans,
Coach Street,
Cork.
Telephone: (021) 271323

Samaritans,
25 Upper Cecil Street,
Limerick.
Telephone: (061) 42111

Samaritans,
14 Nun's Island,
Galway.
Telephone: (091) 61222

Samaritans,
13 Beau Street,
Waterford.
Telephone: (051) 72114

Bereavement Counselling Service,
St Anne's, Dawson Street,
Dublin 2.
Telephone: (01) 767127

Bereavement Counselling Service,
Tabor House, Miltown Road,
Ranelagh,
Dublin 4.
Telephone: (01) 698335

National Association of Widows in Ireland,
12 Upper Ormonde Quay,
Dublin 2.
Telephone: (01) 770977

National Association of Widowers,
c/o 28 Rubens Avenue,
Dublin 8.
Telephone: (01) 536800 (after 6p.m.)

FLAC (Free Legal Advice Centre),
49 South William Street,
Dublin 2.
Telephone: (01) 794239

A voluntary organisation. The local library
has addresses of nearest FLAC offices.

Legal Aid Board,
47 Upper Mount Street,
Dublin 2.
Telephone: (01) 609711

Gives help with non-criminal legal cases and
will provide solicitors at low cost. This
service is means tested.

Prudential Life,
Prudential House,
Mount Street,
Dublin 2.
Telephone: (01) 611922

They publish a leaflet called
Where there's a will. . . There's a relative.

9. Continuing To Work

At 90 Hilary Boyle still earns her living by writing magazine articles and radio scripts. She writes about what she knows; gardening, the environment, social justice, vegetarianism. Her bedsitter in Cabinteely is crammed with books, papers, plants and posters. She has two papers delivered daily, and is completely in touch with current affairs. Her advice is 'never retire, just don't stop working'. This is easier said than done for the majority of the workforce who have to accept arbitrary retirement at 60 or 65. Many are ready to leave when the time comes, they've been winding down, they've plans for the next stage of their lives. Many, but not all. For about one-third, retirement comes too soon: 'I wasn't ready', says Pat, a teacher, 'I felt I could have given many more years in the job, which was far more than just a job to me always'.

As is Charles Deveney's work. He has been involved in his family's grocery business for over 60 years. He can reminisce back to the days when a large sliced pan, and half a dozen eggs cost 1/1d, and the girls used call around the neighbourhood taking daily orders from the woman of the house. Still, he has adapted to changing trends, and now in his mid-70s is bright, fit and alert.

'There is no question of retiring where I'm concerned. It's a matter of control over mind and body. The mind is sending messages to the body all the time, and if the body has nothing to respond to, it's death. I've worked in the family business all my life, and these days, I don't need the money, I would do it for nothing'.

Don't Stop Working

Of course, people with special skills can carve their niche, irrespective of age. Retired RTE newsreader, Charles Mitchel, is an actor by profession, but his television contract precluded any advertising work. Now retired, he can supplement his pension in the advertising field, doing voice overs and making personal appearances. Mollie Keane who lives in Co. Waterford, began writing again at 79, after a long silence while she reared her children. *Good Behaviour* her novel, became an immediate bestseller, and its success has encouraged her to continue. Her routine is precise. She works in the morning from nine to noon and writes in longhand.

Her craft, which reads so fluently, does not come easily to her. 'I hate writing. It is terribly hard work. I own the work in the morning, and then it leaves me in the afternoon. My eyesight, hearing facilities are all good, in fact, I've always been pretty sharp'. Former Taoiseach, Jack Lynch, doesn't see himself as retired, even though he is now left politics. 'I am still involved in public affairs, in a variety of ways as well as being a member of the boards of some business companies. Indeed, I seem to be kept as busy now as when I was actively engaged in politics, so I am not retired in the accepted sense.'

Some people in public life can afford to face retirement with enthusiasm. 'I think people should go and make room for new talent and new ideas', says National Gallery ex-director James White. 'The day I left, I left, and would never dream of interfering now in any way'. Yet James White too stepped into a very busy retirement. A stint as chairman of the Arts Council has been followed with honorary secretaryship of the RDS, plus an involvement with the Chester Beatty Library plus a career in writing.

A Job In Retirement

A job in retirement fulfills four needs: it can provide extra income, where the occupational pension is small or non-existent, it gets people out and offers companionship, it opens the way for new kinds of learning, and gives many retired people a focus and a purpose. Against this must be measured the cost of working in travelling, clothes, lunches and other expenses, and the possible pension and tax losses. People claiming the retirement pension may hold a part-time job involving less than 18 hours a week. Contributory old age pensions and occupational pensions are both taxed in proportion to other earnings and assets.

When Patrick who lives in Louth retired, he took a part-time job which helped his adjustment into the new life. He had been a civil servant for 40 years. 'I found retirement very traumatic. One evening, it was over, I walked away from the whole group, from seeing hundreds of people every day. It happened so quickly, and there was a huge difference between knowing it will happen, and actually experiencing it. 'I felt very strongly I was no longer needed. From being somebody, I was just somebody down the road'. So he set about being needed again. He got himself a morning job as administrator in the local community centre, and held it for six years. 'At the beginning, the job was a reason for me to get up every morning, it passed the time and gave me an interest'.

Jobs for the Over-60s

'But gradually I got into a different routine. My wife and I began to play golf together, we completely redesigned the garden, the job was becoming a tie, and I no longer needed it. So I waited until they got a replacement for me, and then I gave it up'. Patrick was lucky in finding such a bridge into retirement. Jobs for the over-60s, traditionally scarce, have become in recession ever scarcer. One of Dublin's largest employment agencies confirmed they would get only a couple of jobs a year offered to the 60-plus age group. A smaller firm specialising in clerical jobs said there are three areas in which retired people could theoretically score — accounting, engineering and computing — where someone with the right background could have a lot to contribute.

In practice, the number of firms interested in employing someone in late middle age are very few. But retraining is available to those willing to widen career prospects by learning a new skill. FÁS the Industrial Training Authority do not have an upper age limit on their courses, and regard a retired person who wants to work, and is available for work, as still part of the workforce. Their *Start Your Own Business* course could be particularly interesting to an early retiree who wants a change of career direction. Equally the Industrial Development Authority have no age restrictions in the giving of grants and incentives to new businesses. 'In some cases, older people may be at a disadvantage', says the spokesman, 'but they will also be bringing a lifetime of experience and expertise to a project. As far as we are concerned, we offer old people the same package of incentives as young people'.

Finding A Job

And retired people are getting jobs despite the difficulties. Blanche in her early 70s is a supply teacher in a private school. Bernard, a retired managing director, is now a delivery person for a local drapery firm. To many this might seem like a huge come-down, not to him. 'It suits me perfectly. I've no responsibilities, but I'm meeting a great cross-section of people, my days are full and interesting'. These people got their jobs through local contacts, so when job-hunting, it's best to begin locally first. Look at the ads in your community newsletter or local paper. Insert your own ad, highlighting your availability, any special skills. Study the ads in the local shops, are there any jobs there you could fill? Other jobs in retirement I came across included a school warden, a woman doing clothes alterations, and a man selling produce at a local country market. Then look nationally, you may be lucky.

Ideally be one step ahead of the posse, and have your sideline organised before you leave. Peadar trained as a medical technician, but was made redundant half way through his working life, and had to take an unskilled job. However, he set aside a little room at home, making a range of medical prostheses; retired now, with a tiny pension from the firm, his sideline has become very important. It raises his income to a decent level, he does a bit of work every day and says the little job makes all the difference. So as well as looking out for local opportunities and services, it's worth developing a skill now to bear fruit later. The local vocational school will probably have a range of night courses.

Here is an A-Z guide of classes, (mostly craft-type) with earning potential:

Acrylic painting	Gardening
Antique restoration	Jewellery making
Art	Journalism
Basketwork	Knitting
Batik	Lacemaking
Book-Keeping	Leatherwork
Calligraphy	Metalwork
Cane work	Oil painting
Carpentry	Patchwork
Ceramics	Picture framing
Community work	Pottery
Cookery	Sketching
Crafts	Smocking
Creative writing	Start-Your-Own
Crochet	Business
Curtainmaking	Tapestry
Dressmaking	Typing
Etching	Upholstery
Flower arranging	Water colours
French Polishing	Weaving
Furniture restoration	Woodwork

83

Starting A Business

Dorothy Price, 76, didn't need to go to night class to find a money-spinning craft. She learned sewing and knitting as a child, and now works as an outworker for a design firm, putting concealed zips into jumpers. 'I please myself. I'm under no pressure, and can do as much or as little as I want. I usually work for two to three hours in the afternoon. I don't do it so much for the money, but I do save my earnings, and use them to go on holiday every year'. Finally, there is room for a good business idea at any age. John J. Cronin from Limerick had been involved with the scouts for 50 years. A retired fitter, he was appalled at the cost

84

of buying scout tents these days. He felt the traditional tent made from heavy canvas could be cheaper to make and just as practical.

He discovered the fabric was still available, did a feasibility study on manufacture and marketing, and approached AnCO now (FÁS) and Shannon Free Airport Development Company with a scheme to make the tents, giving employment to young people. His plans met with official approval. The company is now in business, the tents, designed by John, are selling well, and he has diversified into boat covers and carrier bags. John, who lives alone, had been quite unhappy in retirement. Today, he is delighted to use his skills again. He is working with young people, creating employment, and is generally happy and fulfilled.

USEFUL CONTACTS AND REFERENCES

Industrial Development Authority,
Wilton Place,
Dublin 2.
Telephone: (01) 686633

IDA Enterprise Centre,
Pearse Street,
Dublin 2.
Telephone: (01) 775655

Branch Offices:

Athlone:
Auburn, Dublin Road.
Telephone: (0902) 72695

Cork:
Norwich Union House,
89 South Mall,
Cork.
Telephone: (021) 968555

Dundalk:
Finnbir Industrial Park.
Telephone: (042) 31261

Galway:
IDA Industrial Estate.
Telephone: (091) 51111

Donegal:
Portland House, Port Road,
Letterkenny, Co. Donegal.
Telephone: (074) 31151

Limerick:
Castletroy House,
Plessey Technical Place.
Telephone: (061) 33400

Sligo:
Finisklin Industrial Estate.
Telephone: (071) 61311

Tralee:
Monvalley Industrial Estate.
Telephone: (066) 25444

Waterford:
Cork Road.
Telephone: (051) 72911

FÁS, Industrial Training Authority,
27 Baggot Street,
Dublin 2.
Telephone: (01) 685777

Branches at:
Athlone - Telephone: (0902) 75390; Donegal - Telephone: (075) 31331; Letterkenny - Telephone: (074) 22200; Sligo - Telephone: (071) 61121; Galway - Telephone: (091) 51260; Ballina - Telephone: (096) 21921; Limerick - Telephone: (061) 28333; Shannon - Telephone: (061) 61133; Tralee - Telephone: (066) 25617; Cork - Telephone: (021) 44377; Dundalk - Telephone: (042) 32311; Waterford - Telephone: (051) 72961; Wexford - Telephone: (0503) 23602.

Shannon Free Airport Development Company,
Shannon Town Centre.
Telephone: (061) 61555

---

10. Voluntary Work

Jack became a Samaritan volunteer eight years ago, shortly after he retired. 'I feel when a person retires, they've got it made. We had reared a family, we've been very lucky, we got a lot out of life, and felt it was time to put a little back'. He was looking for some voluntary work when he saw the ad. 'I was on top of the bus and saw a board with the message "don't say nobody cares, ring the Samaritans". I thought it was grand to realise that people did care, I applied to be a volunteer, and was accepted for training'. Being retired, he's available for day work. He does one duty of three to four hours a week, an overnight stint once a month, and is on call for flying squad duty to respond to an emergency also once a month.

He loves the work. 'Samaritans always get as much out of it as they put in', but stresses it is not a service everyone could give. 'First of all you have to care, be a good listener, and nothing you hear must shock you. You must be unflappable, non-judgemental, and accept people as they are, even if a caller's attitude would differ from your own. No Samaritan imposes their moral standards on a caller. Having said that, you can be so caring that your judgement is affected, and you won't be able to be a source of strength to the caller. You must retain the correct balance'.

Retired People Are Invaluable

A Samaritan director echoes Jack's views. 'Retired people are invaluable to us. They are free for daytime duties, and they understand the difficulties that can be associated with retirement. We liken it to bereavement for some. We receive calls from people, who, in spite of preparation, were not ready for the reality of retirement. Retired volunteers recognise the depression and difficulties which can be associated with the adjustment. But there is a rigorous interview for a Samaritan volunteer, and many retired people who have risen to executive level in their jobs would find it difficult to work within our rules.

'Our emphasis is on listening, not directive counselling, on encouraging people to talk about their problem, rather than coming up with ready-made solutions or suggestions for their problems'. In the area of voluntary work and retired people, imbalances exist. On the one hand, there are hundreds of organisations around the country urgently needing voluntary help, on the other, there are thousands of retired people who could give that help. Why is there not more meeting between the two sides? One reason is that people tend to begin voluntary work in early or middle life, rather than in retirement.

Most retirees I met have been doing good deeds for years. Jack was unusual in beginning in retirement. Tommy McKeown from Malahide who has worked with the St Vincent de Paul Society for years would be more typical. A retired air pilot, he has increased his involvement with SVP, and now spends two evenings a week on their affairs. John retired from the public service four years ago, and was already so taken up in his voluntary work that he had a ready-made second career to step into. As chairperson of his local community council in Galway, John has a busy week.

On Monday afternoon he helps out with bingo at the local centre, on Tuesday and Thursday he delivers meals on wheels. He is a minister of the Eucharist, and on Wednesday morning, he distributes Holy Communion to housebound parishioners. Thursday is St Vincent de Paul night, and this can spill over into family visits on Saturday. He also runs summer outings and socials. 'I liked my job', he says, 'but I don't think I've ever worked as hard since I retired'.

Teaching Literacy

Sean and his wife Sheila are literacy tutors, attached to the Dublin Literacy Scheme. They teach illiterate adults how to read on a one-to-one basis.' Sean spends time building up a relationship, gaining his pupil's confidence before learning begins proper. Progress can be slow, and tutors have to be very patient, as levels of motivation and ability vary so

much. Sean is a retired bank manager. He wanted a voluntary job quite different from the hierarchical structure he worked within. 'I wanted something where I could just be me. I've got a tremendous amount out of it, above all, perhaps an insight into the lives and working conditions of people long ago. The job has made me realise the dignity of each individual, and the value of the work they do, no matter how humble it may seem'.

A literacy teacher may seem the perfect voluntary niche for the retired academic, but not necessarily, according to the scheme administrator. 'We do need volunteers, and some retired people have worked out well, some not. You need patience, some older people get frustrated and upset if, for example, the pupil doesn't turn up as sometimes happens. Ironically the wrong people may be retired school teachers. We find they can be too rigid, too geared into the school system. You need a flexible approach teaching literacy, and often people with no background at all in teaching do best.'

Matching Skills to Organisation

As with the Samaritans, attitude is all-important, skills can be learned. So the whole area of matching person to organisation is an important one. The good news here is that the Retirement Planning Council has set up a volunteer bureau to perform the function of matching individual and organisation. The Council had long felt that this service is needed, and that many more retired people would engage in voluntary work, if they felt their services would be useful and they knew who to contact. The Retirement Planning Council has on file lists of organisations looking for retired volunteer help, broken down into specific categories and job types.

Aspiring volunteers are interviewed on their skills, interests, foibles and availability. They are then put in direct contact with the agencies they would seem to suit best. An informal system along these lines is already working well in Kilkenny, where retired people are positively encouraged to offer their skills. Retired people are contributing to a number of community projects, the Kilkenny Social Service Centre is the contact point, and the scheme is growing and developing year by year. A more established idea works well in England. REACH stands for Retired Executives Action Clearing House. It acts as a channel between people and places, and already has hundreds of satisfied voluntary customers under its belt.

Meanwhile, how can you help yourself to a fulfilling voluntary job? These are the questions you should ask yourself:

What kind of skills or experiences would you have to offer?
Secretarial, handyman, financial, cook — you'll know what you can do.

Have you hidden skills?
Some people are born listeners, the kind others come to for advice. If you're that kind of person, you may be good at counselling and visiting.

How much time would you have?
Voluntary work can last from an hour a month to five days a week. Consider how much time you'd like to offer.

Does physical or mental handicap bother you?
Do you get deeply upset by tragic situations?
If the answer to these questions is 'yes', you should obviously steer away from groups working with disability, neglected children, or family violence.

Have you any strong interests or beliefs?
You may always have been interested in conservation, civil liberties or the third world. Now is your chance to contact an agency furthering those causes.

Are you a leader?
Some people like to lead, others to be led. Agencies need both types, but it is important to know what type you are so you can be channelled properly, and used most effectively.

What agency to approach? Looking at Irish organisations, voluntary work opportunities seem to break down into five main areas: 1. Befriending; 2. Fund-raising; 3. Awareness; 4. Transport, and 5. Office work.

Befriending: These include organisations whose members visit lonely, elderly or housebound people and establish a relationship with them. The Society of St Vincent de Paul has hundreds of local conferences all over the country, and there will be one near you. In Dublin one of the most caring agencies is Alone, started by Dublin fireman, Willie Birmingham.

Fund-raising: Almost every organisation I contacted said they could do with help with fund-raising. There is always a short-fall between what money they get and what they need. They raise money in a variety of ways — annual flag days, sales of work, fashion shows, raffles, auctions. People with public relations abilities, new ideas and organising ability are needed here.

Awareness: Many groups use local committees both to raise cash and raise awareness. I'm thinking particularly of third world organisations who set up local support groups to run film shows, give talks and act as local educators on third world issues. The Mental Health Association of Ireland has local groups too, and do important work in destigmatising the whole area of mental illness.

Transport: Many organisations need drivers. Distances vary, typical runs would involve bringing children from home to clinic, old people from home to day centre, to the doctor, on outings, to parties and pantomimes. If you have a car, and can afford to use petrol in this way, you would be of service. The meals on wheels organisation is dependent on drivers to ensure that the beef and vegetables arrive at houses still piping hot. Depending on area, commitment is likely to be a few hours every fortnight or month.

Secretarial: Many organisations use voluntary staff in their offices each day. For example, the Central Catholic Library, Dublin is always in need of voluntary helpers, and retired people work very successfully in their reference and lending departments. They want people who are free to give a few hours each week. An interest in books is useful, but no library training necessary. With 70,000 books, the library is open until 9pm each evening, and very well used.

Other Possible Areas

Perhaps you have a nice speaking voice? The Irish Association for the Blind uses volunteers to read on to dictaphone in the preparation of taped magazines and books for blind people. Perhaps you're a good granny? The Irish Pre-School Playgroups Association are always interested in grandparents who might like to help out in a local playgroup. Many grannies are good at telling stories, and provide a much-needed extended family dimension for many children. Overall, there are hundreds of organisations to choose from. *Hey You! A Guide to Voluntary Work Opportunities in Ireland* will give a lead into some of them. Published in 1978, it is now somewhat out of date, but still useful as a guide.

What other ways are there to find voluntary work? 'Think local', says Frank Reynolds, head of development, at the National Social Service Council, 'look at the opportunities in your own local community. Go to your social service council if you have one, and see what areas of activity you could contribute to. Try and match what you have to offer with what is needed. And what in many areas people need is a relationship, to break down the loneliness and isolation that has come to be part of today's society.'

Looking around my own area, I find it is voluntary help that runs the meals on wheels, the St Vincent de Paul Society, writes the parish newsletter, organises and runs the summer project, started a parents' drug awareness group, plans a programme of activity for old people, runs the guide, cub, scout and brownie pack, and local youth club, maintains the many sports clubs, and most recently, a local resource group for unemployed people.

I also notice that there are needs not being met; old people not being visited, beaches not being kept clean, town untidy, travelling people neglected. Your area will have other opportunities, other gaps. The reason most people give for helping other people is they get so much themselves out of doing it. One Sligo woman I spoke to visits people in hospital, and says the example of patience and courage she sees are a constant challenge to her.

Paddy Hughes who trained thousands of youthful athletes over the years is still leading his young pack out every Saturday. At 76, he enjoys it as much as any of them. Harry Lynch teaches art to a retirement class in Clontarf, Dublin, and loves it. 'It keeps me on my toes, you never know what questions you're going to meet. I've learnt an awful lot through them'. Many people take up voluntary work as a practical response to the Divine command to 'love thy neighbour'. Also the sense of fulfilment and satisfaction from helping other people makes it all very worthwhile.

USEFUL CONTACTS AND REFERENCES

The Retirement Planning Council,
16 Harcourt Street,
Dublin 2.
Telephone: (01) 783600
Volunteer bureau.

Kilkenny Social Service Council,
Waterford Road,
Kilkenny.
Telephone: (056) 21685
Informational volunteer bureau in operation.

Alone,
3 Canal Terrace,
Dublin 12.
Telephone: (01) 509614

Mental Health Association of Ireland,
6 Adelaide Street,
Dun Laoghaire,
Co Dublin.
Telephone: (01) 841166
Branches around the country.

Concern,
1 Upper Camden Street,
Dublin 2.
Telephone: (01) 681237
Branches around the country.

Gorta,
12 Herbert Street,
Dublin 2.
Telephone: (01) 615522
also at:
25 Oliver Plunkett Street,
Cork.
Telephone: (021) 272056

Central Catholic Library,
74 Merrion Square,
Dublin 2.
Telephone: (01) 761264

Irish Association for the Blind,
8 North Great Georges Street,
Dublin 1.
Telephone: (01) 742349

National Social Service Board,
71 Lower Leeson Street,
Dublin 2.
Telephone: (01) 616422

For social service organisations and community information centres around the country, see references at the end of chapter 5.

The Samaritans have branches in Dublin, Cork, Limerick, Waterford, Galway, (see references chapter 8).

Hey You guide to voluntary work opportunities, published by Wolfhound Press and still available in libraries.

11. Learning — Old Dogs and New Tricks

Eamon Byrne left school at 13-and-a-half when his father died, and he had to find work. He did well in industry, rising to factory manager. He was helped by night classes in book-keeping and commerce, 'but I never had time for education in ordinary living'. He retired eight years ago, and after a fairly difficult period of adjustment, enrolled in a full time communication course at Pearse College, Crumlin. The course consisted of a range of projects around the idea of communication including media studies, personal communication, computer appreciation, reading.

Eamon loved it, and the next year plunged in deeper with a two-year course in European studies in which he learned French, as well as an understanding of modern Europe. He's currently doing a course in cultural studies which covers English and Anglo-Irish literature, music, art, history, social geography, philosophy and politics. These days Eamon is thrilled with himself. 'First of all, I've made a lot of friends. The college here is a community in its own right. There are outings, theatre trips, activities arising out of the various courses'.

More Studies

'The French was tough enough at the beginning, but I persevered with it, and on the trip to France, I was able to get around and meet French people. What I've learned is really affecting me in every way, the books I read, the television I watch, I've become very interested in history. I retired during bad weather, and was stuck in. During the early weeks, my mind would harken back to what they were doing in the office. The time signal for ten o'clock would come on the radio, and I'd think, they'll be having the cup of tea now, and chatting about last night's match. I was lonely.

'But since coming back to school, so to speak, I've never looked back. I haven't enough time in the day, and I think it is important for retired people to have a bit of pressure, to be always a bit too busy, and have things to do'. Nan Duffy is a fellow student with Eamon in cultural studies. She cycles to school every day, and was among the first group of women to enrol in the college. She joined with some other members of her women's club, and they began with a foundation year in basic English, before progressing through communications, European studies to the

91

cultural studies course.

Nan too left school at an early age. 'I never got to secondary school, my children did, and when Pearse College opened I felt it was my chance. I never realised what I was capable of, what was inside me. I'm much more confident than I was before. I've been on lots of trips through the college, to the Gaeltacht, to Europe. It has changed me a lot, I have many more friends, wider interests, and I'm mixing with young people too, age is no barrier'.

You're Never Too Old To Learn

Pearse College, Crumlin is unique as it is the only day-time adult education college in the country. Opened in 1979, by 1985 it had 450 full-time students, 100 of them retired people. College principal, Pat Feehan scotches at the myth that you can't teach an old dog new tricks. 'That's rubbish. You're never too old to learn. The mind is wonderful, particularly if it's kept active, and our minds are working away all the time, far more than we think.

'Take the woman who gives up her career and stays at home to rear her family. Think of the decisions she has to make, the way she must budget, organise — she's mother, doctor, philosopher, teacher, economist. She has the opportunity to have the radio by her, a tremendous amount of education there. She is also bombarded with advertisements, and has to steer a path through them. Think of the changes we have all had to come to terms with as adults in our lifetime. There's been metrication, decimalisation, computers, calculators — it's been ongoing adult learning'.

Nor does he accept that poor concentration (if it occurs), in advancing years is a bar to learning. 'Is education memory? Surely it is far wider than that. True education develops what is inside a person, with the backing of his own life and experiences to draw on'. Certainly the public perception is that as the body slows down, so the brain follows suit. Yet if this were true, the great wealth of scientific and artistic discovery would come from people in their 20s and not, as happens from the mainly middle-aged and older categories.

Old and Past It?

Look at how some old people perform. Winston Churchill was a pensioner before he became prime minister, Cyril Cusack in his 70s, brings new depth, sensitivity and maturity to his acting today. These people are special because society did not demand they retire at 65. That the majority must, does not mean a national reduction in mental ability.

Where does the stereotype 'old and past it' come from? In *Age and Opportunity, Education and Older People*, social historian Eric Midwinter explains that adult intelligence has traditionally been worked out from psychological tests which measure various aspects of mental performance such as reasoning ability and memory. The relationship between age and intelligence has mainly been investigated by comparing the performance of young and old in a standard test involving concept formation, problem solving and abstract thinking.

In most cases, older people perform less well than younger, which used to be interpreted as a sign of a decline in mental faculties across the life span, an age change. But more recent thinking suggests that the comparison of groups of different ages can cast light only on age differences. There are many cultural, environmental and social differences between a 70-year-old and a 20-year-old today, besides the ageing process itself. These include an educational system which has changed greatly over 50 years and an intellectually enriched environment provided by television, books, foreign travel which has influenced the lives of many young people since their formative years.

The results of a newer intelligence-measuring approach are quite different. They suggest that successive generations are becoming more intellectually able, and that mental ability in adult life follows an undulating pattern, sometimes regressing, and the relationship between age and mental ability is very small. The success of Pearse College would tend to bear out international findings. Pupils there range in age from 18 to 72. They've had a grandmother sitting for her Leaving Certificate alongside her grandson, (both successful). Class activities have blossomed into public speaking and debating competitions, theatre and field trips, mountain climbing.

Low Participation in Adult Education

Pat Feehan maintains that because we consistently categorise and limit what people are able to do, many elderly people begin to believe the stereotype. Certainly the number of retired people participating in adult education in this country is very low. Robin Webster, formerly of Aontas, the National Association of Adult Education, puts it at less than 2%. Why such a poor turnout from people with time on their hands? 'There are several reasons. First, adult education is still seen as night classes, and this doesn't suit many retired people, who want something to do in the day, not the evening.

'Secondly and more importantly, for many people retiring today, their education was a primitive, irrelevant, unsatisfactory, unhappy time. 80-90% of those retiring now, left school early. School was something that happened a long time ago, an unattrat-

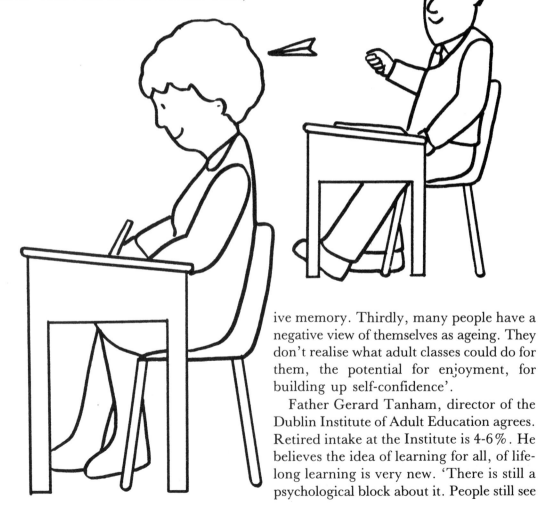

ive memory. Thirdly, many people have a negative view of themselves as ageing. They don't realise what adult classes could do for them, the potential for enjoyment, for building up self-confidence'.

Father Gerard Tanham, director of the Dublin Institute of Adult Education agrees. Retired intake at the Institute is 4-6%. He believes the idea of learning for all, of life-long learning is very new. 'There is still a psychological block about it. People still see education as something you do as a preparation for life, rather than something you can dip into all during your life'. Obviously, in order for adult education to reach more people, it will have to be sold in a new way.

Marketing the Courses

Educationalists I spoke to admitted that they're only coming around to the idea of marketing the commodity. This would have seemed a crassly commercial approach, not any more. 'Take someone with £20 to spend', says Co. Wicklow adult education organiser, Brian MacDiarmada, 'we have to compete for that £20 against all kinds of other forces, and we have to try to be as persuasive as they are'. Pat Feehan has been using his own brand of persuasiveness for years. 'Recruiting students means personal contact with prospective clients, you have to become a salesman. Whole time education will have to be sold and marketed on a very professional basis. It involves contacts with numerous groups, talking to women's clubs, health boards, at retirement planning functions. Recruitment is an ongoing programme, and it's my policy when meeting people to invite them to visit the college and meet staff and pupils'.

Many retired people say they would like to go to classes, but can't afford them. Adult education organisers, for their part, say that inability to pay should not deter people coming. Fees can be reduced, or waived altogether, particularly when the necessary number has already been reached to make a class viable. But retired people are unlikely to enrol for classes they can't pay for, and, indeed the Vocational Education Committees confirms that very few apply for a fees waiver. Also, fees may be only a part of total cost.

Full-Time Education Is Free

Maureen Clancy was made redundant before the age of 65, so doesn't qualify yet for a contributory old age pension, and must manage meanwhile on unemployment assistance. She has fulfilled her life's ambition to go back to school, beginning with Irish class, now graduating on to Leaving Certificate French, and loves it. Unable to pay for books, she got them second-hand from nieces and nephews, but her educational outlay must end there. 'I can't afford the extras, the field trips, the outings. Going abroad with the French class is, of course, out of the question, and even theatre trips organised to coincide with the course are beyond me'.

There are ways around the cost of adult education and Pat Feehan has found one. Since the 1960s, full-time second level education is free for all students. 'There is no upper age limit', says Pat, so he applies the letter of the law. His day students at Pearse College fulfil the required 24 hours a week at class. They are, therefore, regarded as full-time students and qualify for free education. (Part-time leisure course students at Pearse College are charged at normal rates.) But there are other gaps between consumer and product. Jack and Lorna from Limerick decided to take evening classes. Both retired, he was interested in carpentry, she in writing. They attended the enrolment night at their local tech but could find nobody to answer their questions about the courses.

Officials were there to record names and take money, but there was no information available. The couple came away without signing up, and now have time on their hands, which they had hoped to fill. Colleges agree that enrolment is a problem, with crowds of people descending on hard-pressed teachers. A solution could be to spread enrolment over a longer period, to inform the teachers taking names about all the courses, so that they could answer queries. Certainly, counselling/advice is needed to match pupil to course. The fall-off rate from adult classes when the first cold November winds blow, highlights the mismatch that often occurs. It is a waste of resources, and tends to turn people off classes altogether.

Day Courses

But the good news is that day classes which suit retired people are becoming established. They're happening because adult education organisers employed by the VEC are trying to meet people's needs. Typical would be the day curriculum at Bray, Co. Wicklow with a mix of leisure and Leaving Certificate subjects. Over a week, Bray offers daytime classes in Leaving Certificate English, history, French, maths and biology, with art, typing, yoga, aerobics and dressmaking for leisure. The intake of retired people is low, but honour is saved by 77-year-old Patrick Kehoe from Greystones, who studied at Bray, and got his Leaving Certificate.

Around the country, the range of subjects offered in day learning includes English, Irish, maths, social studies, psychology, but the numbers of schools is still low. Facilities for day learning, however, could improve. 'With falling school rolls, buildings are becoming available', says Robin Webster of Aontas, 'the challenge is to hold onto them educationally, and not to see education purely for children, but in terms of lifelong learning. If a group looks for a teacher for a particular course, theoretically a school is bound to respond if there is a place. Much better if a school can respond with somewhere safe and warm for people who want a space to get on with their own thing'.

A new way of looking at education for retired people is to see its potential in providing another resource; instead of seeing them as passive learners, we should regard them as potential teachers. The rationale behind this thinking is that elderly people have a wealth of experiences, precisely because they have lived so long They have held down jobs, raised families, coped with great cultural and technological change in their lifetime. The people retiring today grew up in the 1930s, lived through the second world war, and rapid change since.

University of the Third Age

They have coping skills, experiences, beliefs, memories, knowledge, opinions and maturity. It was to recognise these skills and build on them that the University of the Third Age was founded in France. Defining the first and second ages as childhood/ education and work respectively, and the fourth age, rather sadly, as dependency, the third age is one of post-work activity, a time ideally of expansion and stimulation. So the University of the Third Age is not a building, but a group of activities, a project, an attitude of mind. There are now hundreds of U3A groups in Europe. The essence of the movement is self-help, though some elderly students do organise a curric-ulum with the assistance of a university campus.

In Britain, U3A groups have variously opened a craft shop, run courses in such diverse subjects as glass engraving and book-keeping, and manage a barter bank. It is a burgeoning movement and it has come across the Irish Sea. At time of writing, there are two Irish U3A groups, both the result of cooperation between adult education and health education personnel. In Blanchardstown, Dublin, a talk on leisure ideas from adult education organiser, Tony Downes, to a preparation for retirement course in Spring 1984, has led in easy stages to the formation of a third age group. Activities began with music appreciation, crafts and cards, and broadened into outings and theatre trips. A year later, Tony Downes pulled back, and the group decided on its own destiny.

One section offers courses and evenings to members on practical subjects like DIY and health care, another plans the kind of social outings that members want, a third gives classes in art and languages. In all cases, the role of teacher and pupil rotates regularly. The skills are drawn from inside the group, not from any outside expert. 'This', says Tony Downes, 'is what makes a U3A group different from an active retirement association, which draws teachers from within, but not exclusively so. Also, a third age group will aim primarily for mutual safety, survival, self-fulfilment and skills-sharing'.

'Vintage Years'

In Roscommon, the U3A project is called the 'Vintage Years'. It is on-going, reaching an increasing number of people in the country. Its architect is adult education officer, Tommy Murray, and Western Health Board health education officer,

Martin Carraher. Again, the project is based on the premise that elderly people are a valuable resource, with a contribution to make to their community. The Roscommon programme offers a three-hour session to a group of retired people for eight weeks. It explores the use of leisure, introduces some practical crafts, develops an information/coping/personal development module, and gives people an opportunity to mix, discuss individual problems and exchange experiences.

In the long-term the course is acting as a springboard for local action. The Ballaghadereen group has established a drop-in centre for elderly people, which they staff themselves. Other groups, without premises, have set up rambling groups, informal visits and card games. Groups have also done action research, holding workshops on such topics as loneliness and isolation — what it is, how it can be helped — folklore and local history. The success of the eight week course offers pointers for more learning of this kind. Tommy Murray, founder of the Roscommon project, kept talks short. He found discussion, interaction, demonstration and practical case studies worked best. A mid-morning to mid-afternoon course which included lunch was very popular.

Different Emphasis

'In the past many courses for elderly people were concerned with imparting information, emphasing practical problems, using lectures by "experts" as the chief medium of communication', he says. 'We need to get away from that in both approach and format. In our approach we emphasise the following: promoting attitude change, encouraging relationships, sociability, communication, arousing self-awareness and social consciousness, stimulating self-expression, sense of purpose and activity, strengthening self-confidence and self-reliance, developing coping skills to deal with the effects of change, enhancing self-esteem, human dignity, independence, reinforcing mental as well as physical health, and increasing political awareness'. The west is indeed awake!

USEFUL CONTACTS AND REFERENCES

Aontas,
The National Association of Adult Education,
65 Fitzwilliam Square,
Dublin 2.
Telephone: (01) 612092

Adult Education Organisers:
Carlow:
Christy Glancy,
Carlow Vocational School,
Kilkenny Road,
Carlow.
Telephone: (0503) 31187

Cavan:
Patrick Nally,
Vocational School,
Cootehill Road,
Cavan.
Telephone: (049) 31735

Clare:
Sean Conlon,
Vocational School,
Ennis,
Co. Clare.
Telephone: (065) 24819

Cork City:
Tom Daly/Jim O'Flynn
City of Cork VEC,
Emmet Place,
Cork.
Telephone: (021) 965227

Cork County:
Margaret Buckley,
Floor 9, County Hall,
Cork.
Telephone: (021) 26891 Ext. 311

Mallow:
Sean Uas O Ceilleachair,
Adult Education Centre,
Cullen, Mallow,
Co. Cork.
Telephone: (029) 79163

Skibbereen:
Jerry O'Sullivan,
North Street, Skibbereen,
Co. Cork.
Telephone: (028) 21537

Dublin:
Carmel Geraghty,
Ringsend Vocational School,
Dublin 4.
Telephone: (01) 684498

Kevin Byrne,
St Stephen's Schools,
Northumberland Road,
Dublin 4.
Telephone: (01) 609309

Eric Carroll,
Crumlin College of Business &
   Technical Studies,
Dublin 12.
Telephone: (01) 540662

Adult Education Resources:
Dublin:
Coolock - Telephone: (01) 474253; Finglas - Telephone: (01) 341426; Killester - Telephone: (01) 337686; Dundrum - Telephone: (01) 989283; Blanchardstown - Telephone: (01) 211012; Tallaght - Telephone: (01) 515666; Swords - Telephone: (01) 403419; Clondalkin - Telephone: (01) 519596; Dun Laoire - Telephone: (01) 801666.

Rest of Country:
Letterkenny - Telephone: (074) 21100; Donegal - Telephone: Donegal 705; Loughrea - Telephone: (091) 41411; Galway City - (091) 62138; Tralee - Telephone: (066) 21488; Kildare - Telephone: (045) 65103; Kilkenny - Telephone: (056) 65103; Portlaoise - Telephone: (0502) 21352; Limerick - Telephone: (061) 47688; Carrick-on-Shannon - Telephone: (078) 20024; Longford - Telephone: (043) 5474; Dundalk - Telephone: (042) 34047;

Castlebar - Telephone: (094) 21031; Navan - Telephone: (046) 21447; Monaghan - Telephone: (047) 81833; Tullamore - Telephone: (0506) 51392; Roscommon - Telephone: (0903) 6151; Sligo - Telephone: (071) 5844; Nenagh - Telephone: (067) 31964; Clonmel - Telephone: (052) 21067; Waterford - Telephone: (051) 73195; Dungarvan - Telephone: (058) 56336; Athlone - Telephone: (0902) 2850; Wexford - Telephone: (053) 24109; Wicklow - (01) 862482.

Dublin Institute of Adult Education,
1 Mountjoy Square,
Dublin 1.
Telephone: (01) 787266

Pearse College,
Clogher Road, Crumlin,
Dublin 12.
Telephone: (01) 757731

An Grianán, adult education college of the
Irish Countrywomen's Association,
Termonfechin,
Co. Louth.
Telephone: (041) 22119

(ICA membership not necessary to attend courses).

Extra Mural Departments of:
University Colleges Dublin, Cork, Galway, Maynooth, Trinity College Dublin and NIHE Dublin and Limerick.

12. Hobbies — More New Horizons

Charles Mitchel writes letters, Tommy McKeown flies, Harry Sweeney cooks, Phoebe Pollock paints, the Mertons make award-winning wines, and Dorothy Price goes dancing. People get up to all kinds of things in retirement. In some cases, their hobbies are a result of careful pre-planning, in others they fall into their interest by accident.

As Harry Sweeney did. Retired ten years, he left work prematurely at 58 because of bad health. His wife had a part-time job, so Harry sat at home feeling a bit miserable, until the day she asked him to put the dinner on because she would be late. Harry, who had never cooked in his life, gradually became interested. He went to town, bought a recipe book, began to learn. Today, he's the family cook. He approaches it with flair and adventure, and loves trying something new. His interest has led him to take over the shopping, and he uses his free travel to ramble into Dublin's Moore Street, to get the choicest peppers and fruits. His hobby has made a lot of difference.

Planning Your Hobbies

Tommy McKeown, former Aer Lingus captain had a different approach. Company regulations decree retirement at 60, so Tommy had a full range of activities mapped out. For him, planning was essential. 'I feel waiting until retirement to take up a new hobby is a bit late. It is better to have an interest organised before you go'. The year before he left, he enrolled in the National College of Art & Design evening course and took drawing lessons. His wife paints, and he wanted a hobby they would share. He also planned to learn French and the piano. Now six years later, he enjoys painting, has made a great fist at the French, but the piano lessons were a flop.

He has also continued to fly light aircraft for pleasure. 'I adjusted to retirement more rapidly than I thought I would, and I believe it is vital to keep physically and mentally active. I walk, I swim, I cycle. Mentally, I must keep alert as well, I feel I would have a tendency to be lazy if I didn't discipline myself, and then I could really atrophy'. Philip and Edith Merton are another couple who have carried over hobbies into retirement. Years ago they went to evening classes in wine making, and joined a wine cycle to attend lectures and demonstrations. Over the years they have perfected their art. Their wine-making season begins each March with apricot wine, later they make peach and gooseberry wine from fresh fruit, and in autumn, they gather elderberries and blackberries for true country vintage.

Finding the produce is half the fun. 'The hedgerows are disappearing year by year', says Philip, 'we spend days picking fruit in the country, and bring a picnic with us'. Wine making has become a way of life, she lectures and demonstrates, he judges in annual competitions, and it is a successful shared hobby. Before retirement, many people worry about how they will spend their money. After retirement, they may become much more concerned at how they will spend their time. Retirement offers a present of 2,200 extra hours a year, it's a lot of time, which can become purposeless without a plan.

Hobbies in retirement can give purpose to the day. Most people need such purpose, because they've been used to one so long. We spend our lives working to a goal — meeting sales and production targets, meeting orders, deadlines. There is constant movement, change. In retirement, the goals won't come from work anymore, so we have to make our own. We need goals and purpose to give the necessary bite to our lives. Not all challenges need be monumental. Little triumphs taste just as sweet.

Phoebe Pollock's husband died very suddenly in 1979. A coping, busy woman, she got on with her life, continued to work at home, to garden and walk the dogs. But she was lonely. Her cousin told her about a nearby active retirement association, and Phoebe enrolled in the art class. 'I was always interested in drawing and painting, but never got the chance to try it. First of all we were taught how to mix colours, how to paint, then the basics of drawing'.

Today, Phoebe's house is full of her own land and seascapes. She likes to draw from real life and will paint outdoors in Wicklow, where she lives, as well as going on annual painting holidays.

She attends two art classes a week, plus a woodwork class where she learned to make her own frames. 'I lose track of time when I'm painting, and it gives me a lot of satisfaction, though there's still a big gap between what I see and want to convey, and what actually comes out. Still, I'm seeing life with whole new eyes, and I've made great friends in the class'. A hobby gives a chance to try something new, or to perfect an old skill. People discover they've hidden talents, which is not surprising. After all, many earn their living in jobs that don't suit them.

In the days before career guidance, people took what they could get, and there was little matching between individual and occupation. Many square pegs ended in round holes, and made the best of it for 40 years. Now in retirement, it's not too late to satisfy other sides of a personality, whether it's an interest in crafts, literature, bowls, or horses. So people who have enjoyed backing horses over the years can make a career of it in retirement. A typical routine would be studying the racing pages seriously every week, placing a fairly modest few bets most days, and going across to the local to discuss changing fortunes.

The second important point about a hobby is that unless you choose bird watching or writing, your interest will probably bring you in touch with other people, through clubs, classes and outings. The Health Education Bureau had a slogan 'Contact Kills Loneliness', and it's true. You're not likely to become lonely in retirement if you're charging off to the morning cookery classes, or polishing your shoes for the Tuesday ramble with the walking club.

How To Find Out What's Available In Your Area?

First stop — the local library, which should have a notice board bursting with details of local events, classes and courses. A plug here for the local library, probably a membership must for every retiree. You can borrow books from fiction, to reference and local history. It will order books on request, it has newspapers to read every day, it will be warm in winter and is a lovely place to come for a quiet browse. Next place to check would be the local vocational school or community hall to see what classes/hobby courses they run.

For Dublin readers *Guide to Evening Classes in Dublin* published late summer each year by the Wolfhound Press, gives an idea of the scope on offer. There is everything from accordion to yoga, with healing, orienteering and rug-making in between. While most courses listed take place in the evening, day curriculae are developing as we discussed in the previous chapter. Other parts of the country would benefit from a Wolfhound guide, but local VEC's do publish their own prospectus. This is usually available in early September, with enrolment taking place a few weeks later for classes which begin in late September/early October.

Still don't know what to choose? Here are a few more suggestions of tried and true pursuits.

Local history society: This involves a small group coming together to investigate the history of their area. One such group in north Dublin began by getting information from the library on old ruins and placenames, then they interviewed some of their oldest neighbours about their memories of days gone by. This group is currently writing a local history book. 'It's fun', they say, 'really interesting, and costs nothing'.

Bridge: I met a man who's learning bridge at 93 and doing well. Bridge seems to be a very successful retirement interest. 'I think it's ideal', says one bridge enthusiast, 'it gets you out mixing with a huge age range of people. There is a commitment to your partner, you have to go to bridge, even if you're dying! It's a game that sharpens the wits, it's a challenge, an interest, and very accessible. There's hardly a village in Ireland without a bridge group, and a teacher'.

Gardening: I've seen most beautiful gardens while researching this book, and while most of the couples had been gardening for years, gardening as a hobby can be taken up and expanded in retirement. Garden expert Desmond Kenny was writing a book on gardening for the over-50s when he died prematurely a few years ago, and these are the tips he passed on to me at the time: Adapting your garden to your changing needs may mean substituting troublesome blooms or hardy annuals with perennial shrubs.

He suggested people visit their garden centre at the beginning of the four seasons to see what's coming in, and shrubs should be rotated to give all-year-round colour, growth, foliage, berries and perfumes. He believed a manageable garden needn't mean a dull one, in fact, as the family's food needs change over the years, there is the opportunity to experiment. When gardening for a growing family, you may have concentrated on the staples — carrots, cabbage, lettuce. On your own again, you should try your hand at something more exotic — courgettes, asparagus, sea kale, herbs.

The glasshouse is now rivalling the gold watch as a retirement present, offering an opportunity for seed propagation. There are many tools to make life easier for the elderly gardener — spring-loaded spades, light-weight wheelbarrows, an electric mower. He recommends gardening classes as a way of increasing knowledge, and making friends.

Bowls: Gaining ground here as a popular sport, indoor bowls allows people to play all year round. It's easy to learn, gives a bit of competition, provides exercise through bending and stretching, and gets you in touch with other people.

Swimming: The heated pool is a great boon to us all, and many school pools have spare capacity during the day at times to suit an organised retired group. Swimming scores well for stamina, strength and suppleness, it's extremely pleasant, and a group activity. Never mind your bulges, they won't be seen once you're down.

Retirement Associations

The umbrella body for much retired shennanigans in a few fortunate areas is the active retirement association. These are run for retired people by retired people. There are still only a handful of such groups in existence, with scope and need for more. The first association came into being in 1978, appropriately in Dun Laoire, the town with one of the largest elderly populations in the country. It began quietly with tea and cards in the afternoon in the local community centre.

The idea exploded, passed by word of mouth. Today Dun Laoire has 400 members, and a waiting list. The association organises 31 activities, including language classes, art, woodwork, yoga, DIY, wine-making, home electronics, walking, swimming, bowling, aerobics, gardening, plus social evenings, lectures, outings to theatre and opera. The association is now run by an almost full-time voluntary staff, and has a structure including an executive committee, a house committee which coordinates the weekly activities, and a social committee.

They are fortunate in having premises, four rooms and an office, rent free. They have a supportive VEC, which provides teachers for many of the courses free and gives them a room in the school for the woodwork class. By way of thanks, the association set up, catalogued and now runs the student library in the college, as well as offering literacy classes to backward pupils. This sharing of skills within the community is one of the facets making the Dun Laoire association so successful. 'We give as much as we're taking', says member Tom Murphy 'and that's the way we want it'.

The Federation of Active Retirement Associations

The Dun Laoire experience has encouraged other areas to form active retirement associations, each quite distinct. In Ballygall, north Dublin the association makes full use of the local community centre for bowls, bingo, arts and crafts classes and talent competitions. In Mount Argus, Terenure, they've opted for dancing, swimming, table-tennis, Irish, French and group holidays. The Clontarf association is different again. They have a neighbourly morning once a week, which has been successful in helping people make friends. There are arts, crafts and painting classes, cards, bingo, musical afternoons and concerts.

In 1985, the Federation of Active Retirement Associations was established, with a view to spreading the idea nationally. There has been great interest all over the country, and it is envisaged that there will be a growth of associations throughout the country in the next few years. How to start an association in your area? 'The way', says Tom Murphy, 'is to get a few people together, four to five will do, and elect a committee. Then find premises available during the day, or part of the day, and start small. You can choke yourself with too many ideas at the beginning. See what skills you have in the group. You may have someone who can teach a language, another who does DIY. These could be your first classes, start small and grow from there'.

Finally, when you're thinking of hobbies, think of the retired American aeronautical engineer who has decided in retirement to build a new satellite in his back garden, using surplus stock from the official U.S. space programme. It will take him years. 'I could spend my retirement watching television. I could sit on the back porch, and listen to my arteries hardening. Instead, I've settled for something that could change the course of history, and is much more fun!'

See Appendix page 117 for a full list of Active Retirement Associations.

13. Holidays — New Places

People benefit from holidays in retirement, as much as at any other time. 'I never want to go', says one man 'my wife really has to bully me into it, but I'm always glad she does, and come home much the better for the change.' Some couples use holidays to visit their children who live abroad. Sometimes one of the partners won't fly, so one goes, whilst the other stays at home and as one such couple claimed, the break is good for them both.

Retired people can do well in holidays, both in age discounts, and off-season offers. No longer forced to cram a trip into July or August, they can take advantage of spring breaks and winter specials in the sun. With hotel and tourism interests now trying to extend the holiday season as much as possible, there are bargains to be had in these shoulder periods. Ireland does not have travel agents specialising in holidays abroad for older people, but there are organisations around to streamline the operation. For instance, the National Association of Widows in Ireland organises numerous breaks throughout the year for members. Value is good, because people get the benefit of group travel reductions, all the arrangements, transfers, and accommodation are organised and people leave with a built-in guarantee of company and friendship.

Group Holidays

Similarly, some of the active retirement associations organise holidays for members, as do old folk's associations, voluntary groups and committees organising activities for older people. In the retirement association, there is maximum consultation in deciding on destination. In the Mount Argus association, Seamus Fitzpatrick is the man who carries out the members' wishes. 'We've been to Llandudno several times, we like the hotel so much. We've been to Holland, Belgium, West Germany, we went to France to inflict our newly learned French on the unfortunate natives'.

The group arrangement brings in people who would otherwise not have a holiday. 'It wouldn't happen otherwise', says Seamus, 'there are many retired people with nobody to go on holiday with, and some of them hadn't been away from home for years before we began'. Booking through an organisation also makes it possible to operate a savings club, bringing a holiday within the price-range of many who wouldn't otherwise afford one. The Irish Travel Agents Association has tried unsuccessfully for years to market holidays abroad for older people. Except for group pilgrimages, they haven't been successful.

Perhaps retired people don't want to be stereotyped, and wish to take holidays anonymously like everyone else. Tom and Eveline Murphy make their own holiday arrangements most years. The Fegans have camped with their children for 20 years, and still take off for Europe. They say camping facilities on the continent have improved greatly over the years. A central point of

information would be helpful, however, if only to learn about the special concessions. For example, all European railways operate a system whereby men over 65 and women over 60 get reductions on fares. Shipping companies also offer rebates.

Reductions

Reductions can be good — 50% reduction in fares on the railways of Belgium, British Rail in Great Britain, Finland, France, Greece, Netherlands, Norway, Portugal, Spain, Sweden, and Swiss Federal Railways. A 30% reduction is available on the railways of Austria, Denmark, German Federal Railways, Hungary, Italy and Yugoslavia. There is a 25-50% reduction on Sealink on the Irish Sea, on the B + I Line and the Irish Continental Line, and a 30% reduction on Sealink's other lines.

In order to avail of the Rail Europ schemes, passengers must have a Client Travel Identity Card (CTIC), and a Rail Europ Senior (RES) card. The CTIC card is available at any CIE station on production of birth certificate, or passport as evidence of age (the CIE travel pass is not accepted as evidence). People also need a passport-sized photograph and a £5 fee. The RES card is to be had at CIE's international rail ticket office, and people need both cards when going to buy rail or shipping tickets. The fare reductions apply only to journeys taken Monday to Friday, and weekend travel is restricted — there is no reduction for travel between Friday noon and Saturday noon, or Sunday noon and Monday noon.

Special Interest Holidays

Within Ireland, there is an organised approach to providing holidays for older people through special discounts for people over 60 given by many hotels and guest-houses. The Bord Failte Guide lists a selection of special interest holidays each year such as golf, fishing, crafts etc. and coach tours would be particularly suitable for retired people. Leslie and Olive Mahon are a pair of satisfied customers, they consider them great value, and would go again.

An Grianán, the residential centre of the Irish Countrywomen's Association offers a range of holiday courses in everything from crafts to country houses. You can go on holiday in Kilkenny and learn to make cheese, there are dressmaking weeks available, painting holidays and more.

Worried About Security?

Many people are discouraged from going away because they fear a burglary in their absence. They may be interested in the House Swapping scheme, organised by the Worldwide Home Exchange club in more than 20 countries. The club is a professional international home exchange service and lists properties of owners interested in exchange. They range from cottages, to large houses with swimming pools. Potential home swappers make direct arrangements with one another, and there is a fee for directory listing. The home-swap is open to all age groups, but would be particularly suitable to retired people, who could exchange without the fear of home-wrecking young children.

USEFUL CONTACTS AND REFERENCES

Bord Failte,
Baggot Street Bridge,
Dublin 2.
Telephone: (01) 765871

National Association of Widows in Ireland,
12 Upper Ormond Quay,
Dublin 2.
Telephone: (01) 770977

Home Swap,
Mrs M.J. Baer,
139A Sloane Street,
London SW1.

Rail Europ,
CIE,
35 Lower Abbey Street,
Dublin 1.
Telephone: (01) 300777

CIE Tours Department,
59 Upper O'Connell Street,
Dublin 1.
Telephone: (01) 746301

Operate Young at Heart holidays, coach holidays, early and late in the season for the 55-plus age group.

Ryans Hotels Ltd.,
23 Upper O'Connell Street,
Dublin 1.
Telephone: (01) 741114

Offer special cut price spring and autumn holidays for the over 60s in Westport, Killarney and Sligo.

14. Room For Improvement

Pensions for All: Two men came to Dublin for jobs in 1940. One landed in the civil service, and the other got a job in a drapery, rising over the years to department buyer. I met them both a month after retirement, and was struck by the differences in their lifestyles. The first has a handsome public service pension, which is index-linked, and a well-invested gratuity. He's playing a lot of golf these days, plans a trip with his wife to see a son in the Far East, and life is good.

The second's job had no pension scheme. He is living contentedly enough on a contributory old age pension, but after a life of watching the pennies, he's still doing it. Holidays this year will be a week in Tramore. It seems very wrong that the jobs we fall into almost by accident can dictate a life beyond work into retirement. Pensions should be a right for all. At present they're a hit and miss affair.

While the numbers covered by an occupational pension scheme are rising (50-70% depending on source), only five out of ten people leaving today will receive a pension from their employer, and the amount may be small. A figure of under £10 a week is not uncommon. It's true that many firms do make ex-gratia payments to top up a poor pension, but this money often comes out of the till, it is not guaranteed and if the firm closes down, or goes into liquidation, the payments will stop. A national pension plan has been promised by succesive Irish governments, but not yet delivered, which is not surprising. Making the promise is easy, implementing it, very difficult.

A National Pension Plan

A national pension plan would mean a pension for every contributor. The state would provide the pension with contributions from employer/employee. Nobody is prepared to name a figure, but many commentators believe a national weekly amount would come down at 50% of average industrial earnings, which employers could top up if they wished. The state would be most unlikely to pay out tax-free lump sums to its citizens, but would confine itself to a flat rate pension.

A national pension plan would cost us all more. At present, employers pay about 12% of earnings into the tax fund, employees 8%. Both would react badly to a request for 5% more, the kind of figure

110

that's reckoned would be needed to service a national plan.

Peter Brew, managing director of Irish Pensions Trust and former chairman of the Retirement Planning Council says that national pension coverage would need state action: "It is true that the influence of multinationals and competition for labour will encourage firms to offer pension schemes. There is more awareness, employers are open to the idea, employees and trade unions are beginning to press for it. But there are many thousands of workers in odd work arrangements who work seasonally, part-time and would not be covered. The proportion in pension schemes would probably rise naturally to 80%, no more.

National Pensions Board

And over the past few years the government has moved. Under present legislation there is no requirement for employers to provide pensions for employees, but as we have seen the majority of firms do offer some provision, and the voluntary system works quite well.

But it isn't perfect and there is room for improvement. In May 1986 the then coalition government set up a National Pensions Board involving a wide variety of interests, with employers, trade unionists, and representatives from the professions, self employed and the public service serving on it.

Its terms of reference included advising the government on measures to improve the security of pension funds. This need arose out of some well-publicised cases where businesses had gone bankrupt, depriving workers of pension rights, as the employer had not met his share of the funding over the years, and had now no capital to make it up.

The Board's first report dealt with this issue. While discovering that most pension funds were well handled, they found a problem in the area of access: "Many employees knew too little about their pension entitlement" says Peter Brew, vice chairman of the National Pensions Board, "and we felt there should be greater disclosure and easier access to information within companies.

"We felt there was a need for a national standard. There should be some minimum funding standard which employers would have to meet. We believe this could involve legislation, embodied in a Pension's Act.

"Such an Act could include the right of employees to benefit on leaving service, and the right to appoint trustees to monitor pension managment on behalf of employees.

Pension Transfers

An Act could also provide for pension transfers. At present few schemes provide for transferable pension rights, and if people are moving from job to job, they could end up with a minimum pension, because there wasn't time to build up a good level of contributions. There is a strong case for legislation to make all pension rights transferable, or at least preserve what has been secured, so that built up entitlements remain and be payable at retirement age. In this way, the pension which had moved from job to job would have little bits of entitlement accruing from each, and in total they could amount to an adequate sum.

Self Employed

The second job of the National Pensions

Board was to examine the whole future provision of pensions in Ireland and the relationship between the existing state private occupational sector, and the individual — in other words, a move along the road to a national pension plan.

For Peter Brew, such a national plan could not function without self-employed people: "In order to widen the contribution pool, we needed to bring in all those outside the PAYE net" he said. In the 1988 budget proposals, steps were taken to do just that. The Minister for Finance announced that from the 1988/89 tax year onward, self-employed people were to be brought into the social welfare net.

The long-term benefit this offers to the self-employed is a state retirement or widow's pension at the same flat rate as that paid to the PAYE sector. The immediate disadvantage is that they now must pay a contribution to this pension based on a proportion of their taxable income.

The National Pensions Board had been asked in advance of the budget to examine what level of contribution would be appropriate. They came up with a figure of 6.6% of taxable income. In the event, the Government reduced this to 3% for 1988, with a projected rise to 4% in 1989 and 5% in 1990.

Not surprisingly, this budget measure has come in for criticism. Self-employed people, notably farmers, have complained that they must now pay contributions higher than employed sections, while receiving the same level of benefits.

The PAYE lobby argue that because the employer also contributes, the state top-up to the self-employed sector will be proportionally greater, meaning that PAYE workers are effectively paying for the pensions of the self employed from central tax funds.

It is also commonly perceived that self-employed people do not pay their fair share of tax or health contributions at the present time, so any future level of contribution pitched to taxable income is seen as institutionalising this imbalance. The situation has not been helped by government moves to allow self-employed people use a self-assessment method in calculating their taxable income.

Income-Related Plan

These are difficult issues, and they will not be resolved easily. At present we are a far cry from an income-related national plan, and many other questions would have to be answered satisfactorily before we come close.

Peter Brew poses some of the issues. What type of pension plan should we have? Should it be index-linked to keep pace with inflation? Not all private schemes have this advantage, and many pensions erode in real terms in the years after retirement. He says there is a lot of resentment against public service pensions which are index linked: "There is the kind of thinking that says 'it's not fair, let's take it from them'. Wouldn't it be better if everybody got a measure of index linking? As a nation, if we agree in any year to a wage increase, it should be possible to given pensioners the same sort of increase. The advantage of a National Plan is that it protects the weaker sections of society.

Again how? At present very few investment channels exist which would enable pension funds to match a commitment to an inflation-proof pension. The government does issue small amounts of index-linked stocks, but these are snapped up rapidly and always oversubscribed. Under exchange control regulations, companies may invest only 12½% of their assets abroad. If this were increased up to a 20% ceiling say, there would be scope for more flexibility and choice, allowing Irish companies take advantage of short-term gains. Alternatively, the government could think of providing a good investment medium at home.

International Trends

In the course of its work, the National Pensions Board has been examining how other countries tackle the national pension agenda. Peter Brew says the trend in Britain, Europe, America and Canada is on placing less onus on the state to provide pensions, and more responsibility on employers and employees.

"One of the problems with the development of state and occupational pension schemes has been the taking away from the individual the incentive to provide for her/himself he says, "I believe passionately that people should begin thinking about providing for themselves and their future. Whose responsibility are pensions? These are the kinds of issues that must be addressed, but there must be a mechanism to protect the weak."

This concept is particularly important in a country like Ireland where a minority in employment is now supporting the majority, and where many people on low incomes or in receipt of social welfare would not be in a position to provide for a personal pension.

15.

Old? Me — Never!

Flexible Retirement: A 1978 EEC survey on attitudes to retirement drew a very mixed response. A quarter of the working people surveyed wanted to retire as soon as possible, another quarter were happy to wait until statutory age, and another wanted to go beyond the date that said they must stop. The remaining 25% had no fixed views, and Ireland recorded a particularly high level of 'don't knows'.

My own research would ageee with the international findings. Certainly, a good third of my interviewees hadn't wanted to retire, they felt they could do the job for a few more years and experienced a sense of loss, resentment at having to go. What's the statutory position? For most Irish workers, retirement is compulsory at 65 and, in many cases, 60 for a woman. Under our social welfare code, a person must be 65 to qualify for a retirement pension and 66 for an old age pension. A survey of occupational pension schemes by the Irish Association of Pension Funds showed that 90% of pension schemes had a normal retirement age of 65.

So we go because we have to, not always because we want to, or understand why. The reasons why 65 has been accepted as the normal retirement age have never been

properly explained. There are no particular economic, social, gerontological factors involved. Two reasons for striking an arbitrary age do emerge. One would be to create a movement in and out of employment, another would give employers the legal right to let someone go, rather than waiting for them to move themselves.

But flexible retirement could also lead to early retirement, so movement could continue and it would not be envisaged that people could stay on forever. At present in America the compulsory retirement age is 70. Many countries now provide some flexibility of pensionable ages by allowing pensions to be drawn earlier, or deferred. Some Irish occupational schemes are flexible, but the state pension scheme has no provision either for early retirement or deferment.

Phased or Gradual Retirement: I met Jim, a retired laboratory technician who, a year before retiring, had stopped coming to work on Mondays. Six months later, he stayed at home on Fridays too. 'By the time I had to retire, I was ready', he says, 'I had got used to being at home and had taken up a little voluntary job. I was really looking

114

forward to retirement, and it's working out well.'

One of the problems of retirement is that it's so sudden. There is an abrupt overnight transition from work to farewell. One way of cushioning the shock would be to give workers the option of entering retirement gradually by reducing the time at work in the final months, while still being regarded by employers as a full employee.

There are different ways of managing phased retirement. One is to award workers periods of release between the ages of 60 and 65. Another is to give an extra week's holiday during each six months in the final four years of work. Swedish workers in their 60s may opt for partial pension, while continuing to work part-time. These different ways are working in Europe, and an EEC 1978 survey showed that many workers would like a period of transition between work and retirement. But in Ireland, Jim is one of the lucky ones. Phased retirement Irish style is, at the moment, an option available to few.

Preparation for Retirement: Only 3% of the 15,000 Irish people who retire every year ever receive any formal preparation for their new life. Notwithstanding, many do very well, launch into second careers, find more time for their hobbies and their family. Some do badly, with the mortality rate among men rising temporarily in the years following retirement. A large number get by. They potter about without too much purpose, but never achieve the real potential for the pleasant life that retirement can offer.

Achieving a national profile of retired people in Ireland is difficult. We have little research in the field, and studies of elderly people tend to concentrate on the vulnerable section depending on social welfare, where limited funds effectively dictate a spartan lifestyle. A comprehensive French study into retired people found one third were very active, out learning and campaigning. A second group remained content in family and local life. But a third group, 25-30%, came into the category of the spectator. They spent a lot of time watching television, eating, sleeping. There is no reason to believe that an Irish survey would be very different in its findings.

Preparation for retirement courses, do not, of course, guarantee a happy 20 years, nor graft on ability-to-cope skills. But most people I spoke to who attended one, found the course helpful both practically and in the questions it raised on attitudes and relationships. If retirement courses were offered within Irish industry ten to 15 years before retirement, rather than in as many months or weeks before, they could be valuable. They would alert people to the financial provision they may need to make, the real need for hobbies and interests; they could be a great help.

But selling pre-retirement courses is difficult. Employees don't demand them, trade unions don't push for them, and employers don't seek them. This apathy seems very short-sighted. Becoming worried about retirement at 60-plus is too late. Bob Carroll, secretary of the National Council for the Aged makes the point that selling retirement courses in industry will be difficult as long as the public perception of retirement is negative. People won't want to get involved in preparing for something they'd rather not think about anyway. Attitudes will have to change.

Retirement Planning Council

One of the chief attitude-changing bodies is the Retirement Planning Council, which has been very successful in organising and running in-service retirement courses around the country, as well as launching a crop of retirement-awareness raising days and adult education courses. The Council also offers early retirement courses and will soon be offering courses in mid-life planning. But with a staff of two, and a small budget, it can only do so much. Even if the Council succeeded in educating more people in the need for retirement planning, it could not cater for a bigger demand unless its operations were expanded.

The case for retirement preparation rests not only on humanitarian grounds, but can be justified economically. The courses are comparatively cheap to implement. They aim to prepare people for a healthy retirement, encourage them to use their leisure and ability to contribute on a local level. Effective programmes would help reduce the need for costly support services for elderly people.

The Future: Every week at our prayer meeting someone prays for 'the old and the lonely'. While half of me becomes angry at the glib stereotype, the other acknowledges its validity. Many elderly people are lonely. They are poor, in bad health, and live in sub-standard houses. A clutch of surveys in urban and rural Ireland in the past few years all testify to this, and organisations such as the Society of St Vincent de Paul and the National Council for the Aged have made the needs of elderly people a special focus.

While this book is aimed primarily at the middle-aged, elderly people can't be ignored in any discussion on retirement as they are literally a growing factor. According to the National Council for the Aged 1985 statistics, by 1991 there will be a projected over-65 population of 387,900 in Ireland, representing 10.6% of the total. Within this, the numbers aged 75 and over are projected to increase at a faster rate than the population as a whole. It is further estimated that by 1991, there will be 20,000 elderly single male households. There will also be 53,800 elderly female single person households, representing a 31% increase in the figures for females in just over a decade.

As people move from their 60s into their 70s, they depend less on earnings from employer, on savings, and more on state pensions. The longer the period since retirement, the less the value of the savings and the greater the reliance on pensions. Also, as people get older, they have increased need for health and social services, particularly the over 75s and those living alone. All this points to the need for a properly coordinated approach to services for elderly people. The Ad-Hoc Committee of the Joint Working Group on the Needs of the Aged recommends that a properly planned approach to a comprehensive service would involve the following steps:

Understanding:
The process of ageing, and the distinction between both calendar and biological age.

Knowledge:
Of the needs and value of old people, achieved through surveys (including local self-survey).

Planning:
By establishing at the beginning what is generally considered a civilised norm of provision.

116

Action:
At national, regional and local level to achieve a coordinated continuum of care available to those who need it, when they need it, at the level they need it and for as long as they need it.

Will:
Both statutory and voluntary to make this happen.

Attitudes:
'Old people are not aliens' wrote a nine-year-old in a school essay some years ago. Indeed, they're not. They're people like you and me; whose only common denominator is that they've been around longer than most. The elderly population is not a homogenous group. Collectively they have as huge a range of attitudes on money, sex, religion, politics, fashion as any other section of the population. It's incorrect to regard them as an amorphous mass, and a noble, self-sacrificing one at that.

Older people aren't any nicer than younger fry. They are boring, cruel, selfish, good-natured, patient, brave just like everyone else. They are no less intelligent, belligerent, resourceful than another section of the population. A change in public thinking about old age is long overdue.

To a society dedicated to the cult of youth, young may be beautiful and age unattractive. Superficially, it can be. Many elderly people also have in common a welter of spare tyres, varicose veins, thinning hairlines and arthritic joints. But looks aren't everything, and for those willing to go deeper than appearance, the rewards are in sharing in the experiences and memories, often hilarious, frequently wise, of a long life.

It is only by allowing ourselves to regard the elderly population as different, separate, that we can accept a lower lifestyle for them. Why should we take it for granted that many old people will and do live in poverty? It shouldn't be that way, it needn't be. At the very least a degree of self-interest should give us pause. We will all be old one day. What kind of society awaits us then?

117

Active Retirement Associations (May 1988)

USEFUL CONTACTS AND REFERENCES

List of Association Officers

Note: On the following list the *first* name is that of the *Chairperson*, the *second* the *Secretary*.

Active Retirement Associations:

DUBLIN AREA

Aughrim Street:
Ms Lily Brady,
43 Benedair Road,
Oxmanstown Road,
Dublin 1.
Telephone: (01) 383132

Artane/Raheny/Killester:
Ms Phil Burgess,
43 Brookwood Road,
Artane,
Dublin 5.
Telephone: (01) 310939

Mrs Rita Murphy,
62 Brookwood Road,
Artane,
Dublin 5.
Telephone: (01) 316966

Blackrock:
Mrs K.M. Underwood,
9 The Elms,
Mount Merrion Avenue,
Blackrock,
Co Dublin.
Telephone: (01) 884548

Ms Lily Kinsella,
8 Green Road,
Blackrock,
Co Dublin.
Telephone: (01) 886490

Beechwood:
Vincent Farrington,
16 Merton Drive,
Ranelagh,
Dublin 6.
Telephone: (01) 973252

Patricia Stanley,
10 Cowper Gardens,
Ranelagh,
Dublin 6.
Telephone: (01) 971888

Blanchardstown:
Mrs Mary Hunter,
17 Roselawn Drive,
Castleknock,
Dublin 15.
Telephone: (01) 213755

Miss Mollie O'Neill,
9 Park Road,
Navan Road,
Dublin 7.
Telephone: (01) 383214

Cabra West:
Mrs Marcella Kenny,
151 Dingle Road,
Cabra West,
Dublin 7.
Telephone: (01) 306132

Mrs Rose O'Driscoll,
136 Carnlough Road,
Cabra West,
Dublin 7.
Telephone: (01) 381377

Clontarf:
Mrs K. Hynes,
Shanvas,
57 Seapark Drive,
Clontarf,
Dublin 3.
Telephone: (01) 337208

Ms Sheila McCarthy,
21 Dollymount Grove,
Clontarf,
Dublin 3.
Telephone: (01) 333062

Crumlin:
Robert Carroll,
7 Captains Avenue,
Crumlin,
Dublin 12.
Telephone: (01) 552560

Christine O'Callaghan,
24 Esposito Road,
Crumlin,
Dublin 12.
Telephone: (01) 507367

Donnybrook:
Patrick Schofield,
7 Brookfield,
Anglesea Road,
Dublin 4.
Telephone: (01) 689563

Theresa Farrell,
7 Pembroke Cottages,
Donnybrook,
Dublin 4.
Telephone: (01) 694198

Dun Laoghaire:
Tom Murphy,
17 Rose Park,
Dun Laoghaire,
Co Dublin.
Telephone: (01) 807968

Mrs Mary Brady,
3 Gort na Mona Drive,
Cornelscourt,
Dublin 18.
Telephone: (01) 859568

Drumcondra:
Harry Potter,
50 O'Daly Road,
Dublin 9.
Telephone: (01) 375576

Ms Doris Ryan,
99 Home Farm Road,
Dublin 9.
Telephone: (01) 377674

Dundrum:
Mrs Bridie Schweppe,
6 Upper Main Street,
Dundrum,
Dublin 14.
Telephone: (01) 980571

Mrs Marnie Scanlan,
45 Highfield Park,
Dundrum Road,
Dublin 14.
Telephone: (01) 984383

Finglas West:
William Devine,
331 Casement Road,
Finglas West,
Dublin 11.

Mrs Sheila Darcy,
227 Cappagh Road,
Finglas West,
Dublin 11.
Telephone: (01) 347639

Foxrock:
Mrs May Dunne,
'Liseaux',
Stradbrook Road,
Blackrock,
Co Dublin.
Telephone: (01) 841009

Mrs M. Synnott,
8 Foxrock Court,
Kill Lane,
Dublin 18.
Telephone: (01) 893079

Guinness:
Mrs Hilda Madden,
Furry Lodge,
Glencullen,
Co Dublin.
Telephone: (01) 955545

Ms Aileen Russell,
Bi-Centary Centre,
St James's Gate,
Dublin 8.
Telephone: (01) 985024

Haddington Road:
Mrs Breid Cahill,
103 Cedar House,
Sussex Road,
Dublin 4.
Telephone: (01) 602710

Harrington Street:
Thomas Comerford,
42 Lennox Street,
Dublin 8.
Telephone: (01) 539880

Mr John Lawler,
33 Lennox Street,
Dublin 8.

Inchicore:
John McEvoy,
5 Golden Bridge Avenue,
Inchicore,
Dublin 8.

Ms Teresa Egan,
75 Emmet Road,
Inchicore,
Dublin 8.
Telephone: (01) 536695

Marino:
Mr J.J. Murran,
55 Annadale Drive,
Dublin 9.
Telephone: (01) 374297

Mr J. Donohoe,
20 Brian Road,
Marino,
Dublin 3.
Telephone: (01) 334688

Mount Argus:
Mr Patrick Lavery,
76 Stanaway Road,
Dublin 12.
Telephone: (01) 977944

Ms Beatrice O'Carroll,
54 Larksfield Gardens,
Kimmage,
Dublin 6.

Mount Merrion:
New Association being formed.
Contact: Dermot Power,
56 North Avenue,
Mount Merrion,
Dublin 6.
Telephone: (01) 889131

Templeogue (Willington & District):
Newly formed group.
Brendan Timbs,
16 Cypress Grove,
Templeogue,
Dublin 6.

PROVINCIAL AREAS

Bray, Co Wicklow:
Mr Brendan Nolan,
15 Glendale Drive,
Bray,
Co Wicklow.
Telephone: (01) 863326

Ms Gabriel Reilly,
Kingsmill Road,
Bray,
Co Wicklow.
Telephone: (01) 862256

Limerick:
Mr Jerry Hogan,
St Josephs,
9 Ashbourne Park,
South Circular Road,
Limerick.

Mrs Pat Clark,
128 Ballinacurra Gardens,
Limerick.
Telephone: (061) 29604

Waterford:
Mr A.J. McCarthy,
Rosemount,
Corr Road,
Waterford.
Telephone: (051) 72341

Mr Batt O'Mahony,
1 Lismore Park,
Waterford.
Telephone: (051) 73767

Wicklow:
Mr John Kane,
Hillside House,
Wicklow.
Telephone: (0404) 67131

G. Cooney,
Kilpoole,
Blainroe,
Co Wicklow.
Telephone: (0404) 68367